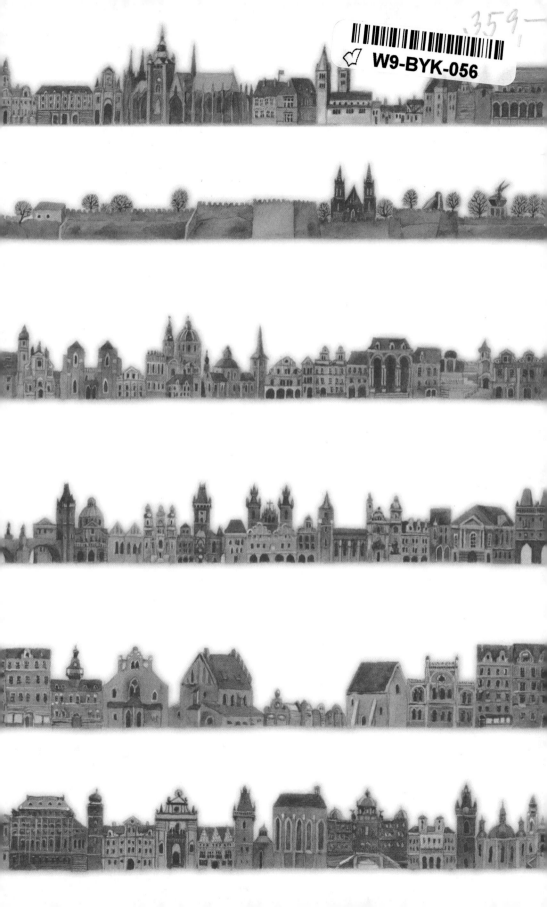

77

Prague Legends

77

Prague Legends

ALENA JEŽKOVÁ

Contents

The old Town

THE OLD TOWN

Vltava

18

17 16

Revoluční

Josefov

15 Dlouhá

Nám.
J. Palacha

Kaprová

12 Nám.
Republiky

4

3

Staroměstské
náměstí

5

11

2

Celetná

10

1

Železná

24 22 21

26

6

13 Ov. trh

23

20

9

Příkopy

25

8

7 19

28

14

Uh. trh

27

Národní Třída

The Old Town Astronomical Clock
The Old Town Hall, Old Town Square 3

The Old Town Astronomical Clock has been telling the time on the south side of the Town Hall Tower for almost six hundred years. The originally simple clock was constructed before 1410 by Mikuláš of Kadaň, but at the end of the fifteenth century it was altered and perfected by Master Hanuš of Růže, who turned it into a unique work unparalleled elsewhere in Europe. Naturally, the Old Town councillors were very proud of the clock, and consequently dismayed when rumours began to circulate that Master Hanuš had received commissions from elsewhere, and was sitting in his parlour long into the night, calculating and drawing something. What else could it be but a clock even finer and more perfect, but destined for some other city? And what then would become of the glory of the Old Town clock? The councillors began to rack their brains to think of a way to make sure the Master would never make another clock for anyone. They thought long and hard, but nothing seemed safe enough, neither offering him money, nor seeking to extort a written bond or solemn promise. Then one of the councillors, a cruel and hard-hearted man, came up with an idea that at first appalled all the others. It was a dire plan, but one councillor after another gradually came round to the view that it was the only way to ensure that the Prague clock would remain unique forever.

One night, Master Hanuš was sitting at home poring over his plans and sketches. It was late, his assistant and his housekeeper had left hours earlier, and the master was alone in the house. Outside it had started to rain, but inside it was warm and cosy. The flickering candlelight drew its own strange figures on the walls, the fire blazed in the hearth and sometimes a beech log would crackle in the silence. Master Hanuš bent over his parchments with their columns of tiny figures, calculations and complicated diagrams, sometimes raising his grey head, thinking for a moment and then writing another note, or crossing the last one out with a frown. He was thinking of how to improve the Old Town Clock, and inventing new, even more extraordinary components for it.

Suddenly there was a sharp knock at the main door and a voice called out,

"Open up, we are in haste!"

The master hurried to the door and slid the heavy bolt from the lock. In the rectangle of darkness he made out the tall figures of three masked men, who rushed at him and dragged him back into his parlour. They gagged him, and two of them held him down while the third went to the hearth, thrust a dagger into the flames and waited until it glowed red hot. Realising what the men intended to do, Master Hanuš let out a stifled scream and fainted with horror. He awoke in unutterable agony. He knew he was lying in his own bed, and he could hear the voice of his assistant and the lamentations of his housekeeper, but he saw only darkness. He had been blinded.

For a long time Master Hanuš lay sick, either delirious or spending whole days in a swoon. His sight was lost forever. When he had recovered a little, he would sit in his parlour and try to think who could have done so terrible a thing and why? Until one day his assistant came back from the Town Hall where he had been cleaning and maintaining the clock and told his master that he had overheard two councillors conversing. They had been congratulating themselves on a job well done, saying that now there was no danger whatever that Master Hanuš would ever make another astronomical clock.

Thus the master discovered who it was that had ordered him to be blinded. He no longer felt pain, just an abysmal bitterness and misery at the way he had been rewarded for his peerless masterpiece. After bitterness came anger and the desire for revenge, followed by a plan to pay his former employers back. One day he told his assistant he would like to go to the town hall so that he might at least feel his beloved clock beneath his fingers, stroke its cogs and wheels, and hear its whirr and tick. His assistant was glad to guide him there.

When they stood in front of the great machine, the master gently touched its parts with his fingers, listened to the sound of the mechanism, and stroked the metal and wood with his palms. His face lit up, and tears sprang from his extinguished eyes. In his mind's eye, he could see the whole complex mechanism before him, each part neatly interlocking with the others, down to the last detail. He reached an experienced hand into the machinery, and pulled at a gear with all his might until it snapped. The clock started to clank, scrape and rattle, until its sounds faded away into an ominous silence. And in that silence the master's heart broke and he fell lifeless to the floor.

The clock seemed broken for good. It was to be many long years before someone was found who could mend it. And throughout those years, the terrifying silence of the clock continually reminded the councillors of their dreadful deed.

The Twenty-Seven Beheaded Bohemian Lords
Old Town Square

Twenty-seven white crosses on the paving on Old Town Square commemorate one of the saddest events in Czech history. It was here, on the 21st of June 1621, that the Czech lords who had led the Rebellion of the Estates against Emperor Ferdinand II were executed. Ten noblemen, five Prague burghers and two burghers from Kutná hora and Žatec were all beheaded by the Prague executioner Mydlář. The Czech lords who met this dismal end included some of the leading noblemen of the land. Among them were the seventy-four-year-old scholar and writer Václav Budovec of Budov and the traveller Kryštof Harant of Polžice, as well as the celebrated physician and professor of Charles University Jan Jesenius, who conducted the first public autopsy in the Bohemian Lands. The dreadful and sorry spectacle lasted from five o'clock in the morning until one o'clock in the afternoon. The heads of twelve of those executed were then hung in iron baskets from the parapet of the Old Town Bridge Tower as a warning to others, six facing the Old Townand six facing the Lesser Town. When permission was given for the heads to be taken down ten years later, relatives and friends buried them at an unknown site. They are said to be interred in the walls of the Church of Our Lady before Týn, or perhaps somewhere

13

in the Church of St Saviour's in the Old Town. According to legend, each year on the day of their death, the 21st of June, the ghosts of the executed gather at the clock and check that it is working properly. If it is telling the time precisely, they are satisfied that the Bohemian lands are prospering, but if the clock is broken, they return to their eternal resting places sad and dejected.

The Bell in the Tower of the Týn Church
Church of Our Lady before Týn, Old Town Square

In the Old Town there once lived a rich but wicked noblewoman. She was such a tyrant with her servants that none of them stayed in her service for long. One day a sweet and quiet rural maid entered her service. She tried to please her ladyship in everything, but without success. Like all the others, all she received for her pains were insults and blows. One evening the noblewoman was preparing to go on a social visit, and the maid was helping her dress, when the bell rang in the tower of the Týn Church to call people to evening prayer. Hearing the bell, the girl stopped attending to her lady, knelt and began to pray as she was accustomed to do at home. The noblewoman erupted in fury.

14

"I pay you to work, not to pray, you lazy hussy!" she shouted, and, beside herself with rage, she flew at the wretched girl, caught her by the throat and squeezed and cursed until she realised she was shaking a lifeless body. Only then did the lady come to her senses. She quickly called the other servants to her aid, but to no avail. The girl could not be revived.

The lady was called to answer before a court, but because she was rich, she managed to bribe the judge and avoid punishment. She thought she would soon forget the whole business and live the same carefree life as before. But every time she heard the bells ringing from the Týn Church, they reminded her of her wicked deed. In the end her conscience tormented her so dreadfully that she gave all her property to the poor and entered a convent, but first she had a small bell cast and hung it in the tower of the Týn Church, where it would ring in memory of the dead girl.

The Palace of the Kinskýs
The Kinský Palace, Old Town Square 11

The beautiful Rococo palace of the Kinskýs on Old Town Square was built in the eighteenth century by the architects Kilián Ignác Dientzenhofer and Anselm Lurago for Count Goltz, and only later did it come into the hands of the Kinský Counts. The palace is striking for its position; it looks as if it has proudly stepped out from the ranks of the surrounding houses and into the square to emphasise its distinction.

The tale goes that when the architect showed the count the preliminary sketches for the palace, he also showed him how splendidly the palace would stand out if it was conspicuously set forward from the row of houses beside it. Count Goltz was enthralled by the idea, but he knew it would be very difficult to arrange. First he respectfully asked the Prague councillors for permission to build the palace further out onto the square, but they considered the very idea a piece of impudence and refused to countenance it. He therefore met secretly with three councillors who had a reputation for being fond of money. He flattered them, argued persuasively in favour of his plan, and when he also offered a large sum of money, they agreed to grant permission. The clever count was aware that the battle was not yet over. He had a large fence built around the site so that no-one could see precisely where the foundations were being laid, and so for a long time nobody had any inkling that there was anything suspicious about the count's construction work. And by the time the walls of the palace had risen above the fence, it was too late to change anything. The infuriated councillors immediately called the count to the town hall, demanding an explanation and the immediate demolition of the building. But the count played the innocent and showed them the official planning permission. The three corrupt councillors went white as ghosts, especially when the count readily revealed who it was that given him the planning permission and how much money he had been forced to pay for it. There was a huge scandal and the three dishonest councillors ended on the gallows. And the palace? It was left where it was.

The Turk from the Ungelt
Týnský dvůr

The Ungelt, or the Týn Court as it is also called, served from early times as the royal customs house. Merchants from faraway lands would offer and sell their goods here, and reside here and meet in its taverns and inns.

One local innkeeper had a very beautiful daughter, but her heart was made of stone, and no suitor was good enough for her. Until one day some Turkish merchants arrived. Among them was a young Turk with dark, bewitching eyes, and as soon as the two set eyes on each other, a passionate love blossomed between them. Days and weeks passed as the lovers met in secret every night and told each other they would never part, but then the time came when the Turks began to think of returning to their native land. The young Turk promised he would come back and the girl promised she would wait for him.

When the merchants had gone, the innkeeper's daughter was inconsolable. She moped and worried for months on end, but her beloved did not come back. Meanwhile, another young man, a local boy, began to court her. He followed her every step, wrote poems for her and sent her flowers. And so the inevitable happened: at first the girl rejected his advances, but when the Turk failed to return, she fell in love and agreed to a wedding.

Alas, fate decreed that the Turk should reappear in the Týn Court on the very day that the innkeeper gave his daughter in marriage. As soon as the Turk saw his beloved dressed as a bride, his brown face turned grey, and when the bride spotted him among the wedding guests, she almost died of fright although she hid this well. When the evening came and the wedding party in the inn was in full swing, the Turk pressed a message into the bride's hand, asking her to come for one last rendezvous at their secret meeting place and saying that he wished to say goodbye. The bride felt sorry for the Turk, and so slipped away from the inn unobserved and hurried off into the night. From that moment on, she was never seen again. People looked here, there and everywhere, and even wondered if she were dead, but nobody suspected the Turk. After all, nobody had known of their love, and even if someone had known, the Turk was soon back in his homeland.

Several years went by until one day a neighbour's girl came running from the cellar screaming that there was a human head under a pile of kindling. The wretched parents and groom realised from the long blonde braids that this was the head of their lost daughter and bride. And nearby they found the rest of her body, still dressed in wedding robes. The murderer was never brought to justice, but the legend goes that he found no rest in death. The ghost of the young Turk walks the Ungelt at night, sometimes carrying the girl's head by its blonde braids.

Three Sisters
Malé náměstí 3

The House at the Three White Roses stands on Malé náměstí (Small Square). In its current form, with a façade decorated by the painter Mikoláš Aleš, it is better known as the House U Rotta after the Rott ironmonger's shop that used to be there. Three white roses are painted on the facade in memory of the legend that gave the house its original name.

Once, long ago, three girls lived here, beautiful and innocent as white roses. Their parents died prematurely and left the sisters great wealth, but they had no idea how to use that wealth wisely, and soon became proud and stupid. From morning to night they would sit in front of their looking glasses, combing their hair, trying on dresses and jewels and gossiping about young men and marriage. They all had the same dream, which was that three rich and noble grooms would arrive and carry them off to castles in foreign lands. And indeed, a handsome foreign prince appeared among the suitors and started to court the eldest sister. He talked for so long about his beautiful palaces over the sea, and the diamonds he would give her and the balls he would hold in her honour that the spellbound beauty agreed to leave with him. She packed her dresses and jewels in heavy chests, her sisters paid her share of the guilders and off she went with her beau. The remaining two girls did not grieve long for their sister. Soon a new face appeared among the throngs of their suitors. A good-looking and wealthy duke from some far-off land began to court the middle sister. He sent her baskets of flowers, precious rings and necklaces, and after a few weeks he took her off to his dukedom together with all her property. The youngest sister was left alone, but not for long, since a young English nobleman turned up in Prague on business and had eyes only for her. He told her about his estates full of parks and gardens, and how she would be a lady with her own chateau on an island in the middle of the sea. What girl could resist? The youngest girl packed up all the remaining property, the trunks were all stacked in a carriage and the driver cracked his whip. The house on the Small Square was left silent and deserted.

Long years passed and no-one heard any news of the sisters. Until one day a travelling journeyman arrived in Prague and recounted all he knew. Three rich grooms for three proud sisters! Not at all...they had all been the same man, a swindler who had only been interested in the girls' wealth. He had taken them off to foreign parts one after the other, robbed them there and left them in misery and poverty until one by one they fell sick and died. Pride comes before a fall and love is blind. Alas for three sisters who never heeded this wisdom...

The Headless Templar
Liliová

In Liliová Street in the Old Town a headless man appears every night on a huge white horse that breathes out sparks of fire. The rider wears a white tunic with a red cross, a sign that he is the ghost of a Templar Knight from the former Templar Monastery of St Anne. In one hand he grips the reins of his restless horse, and in the other he grasps his own severed head. They say that he was beheaded for some offence and shortly before his death he abandoned the Christian faith, for which he was placed under a curse. He is still waiting to be released from it, but he can only be set free by a dauntless youth who will catch the horse by the bridle, seize the knight's own sword and stab him with it through the heart. And such a youth is yet still to be found.

The Three Savages
Řetězová 7

In Řetězová Street in the Old Town stands a house with two savages painted on its façade. There used to be three, but time has erased one from the plaster. A merry tale is told about the savages who gave the house its name. The story goes that sometime in the eighteenth century a foreigner came to Prague bringing with him three savages from faraway America to show the public how they lived. The performance was a grand one. Dressed only in leather skirts and with feather head-dresses, the Indians danced and capered, jumped high, shouted in a strange tongue and even tore live pigeons up with their bare hands and ate raw meat in front of the astounded audience. All Prague soon came to see the spectacle and the foreigner was making money hand over fist.

A peasant from South Bohemia who had come to Prague on business was one of the many who wanted to see the savages from America with his own eyes. He paid, sat down on the bench and watched the performance, his mouth agape. Only something about the savages didn't seem quite right to him. Suddenly he realised what it was, and shouted out for the whole hall to hear, "Frankie, Alois, Vince! What on earth are you doing here?"

The savages froze, but although they then continued their dance as if nothing had happened, the farmer was right. He called out again to the whole hall, "Good people, I've known these savages for years. They're just grooms from our manor in fancy dress!"

When news of the deceit spread the next day and the local government office began to take an interest in the matter, the foreigner and his savages were nowhere to be found.

The Fiery Man
Karlova

In one of the houses on Karlova Street there once lived an old moneylender. He lent money to people in need, but his interest rates were so high that few could ever pay it back, and the moneylender knew no pity. He had deprived more than one poor man of the roof over his head. As his wealth grew, so too did his fear for his money; he was friends with no one, scarcely ever went out, and when his neighbours saw him on the street he never even returned their greetings and would hurry quickly away. Every evening the light in his house would burn long into the night as he counted and recounted the gold pieces in his chest.

One night a fire broke out in Karlova Street. It began in the house just next door to the old money lender. The neighbours from the whole district ran out and helped to fight the fire, carrying crying children out of the burning building and assisting with buckets in any way possible. Only when the flames had engulfed the roof did

the old money lender run out of his door, but it was not to help. The neighbours called out to him, but he said not a word and trotted off in the direction of the Vltava River with a heavy bag containing his money over his shoulder. That was the last time anyone saw him alive.

After a while, however, his ghost started to haunt Karlova Street. Around midnight it would totter down the street with its heavy burden on its shoulder asking for aid. It is said that anyone who helps him carry the bag of money from Karlova Street to Old Town Square will free the soul of the unhappy usurer. The trouble is that whenever some passer-by feels sorry for him and comes closer, the old man turns into a fiery skeleton with burning coals instead of eyes and so the would-be Samaritan quickly changes his mind and takes to his heels.

The Iron Knight
Platnéřská

In Platnéřská Street in the Old Town there once stood a house where a young girl lived. Her beloved was a hot-blooded knight, who guarded his love like a dragon his treasure. One day he thought she was making eyes at another man, and so he stabbed her with his sword in a jealous rage. Before the innocent girl breathed her last, she put a curse on her lover. As she expired he turned into iron, with no hope of release unless another virgin should take pity on him – and this could only happen on one night every hundred years.

The decades went by, and then the centuries. Owners and tenants came and went in the house, and in the end no-one lived there who could remember the story of the cursed knight and his beloved. A widow moved into the house with her charming daughter. The lady was vigorous and confident, while her daughter was the complete opposite, meek and mild. One evening the mother went to bed early, leaving the daughter sitting in the kitchen by the oil lamp, embroidering linen. The night was silent, the moon was full and the moonlight shone through the window. Suddenly a chill gust of wind shook the lamp. The startled girl looked up from her sewing. She heard a melancholy sigh, and the clank of iron, and a tall figure clad from head to toe in ancient armour appeared in the room. The man had the visor of his helmet pulled low, his long black robe hung down to the ground and his right hand in its iron sleeve rested on his sword hilt. The girl was so terrified that she couldn't speak, stopped sewing and trembled all over. "Don't be afraid," the knight told her in a hollow voice, "I am the iron knight, and I have been compelled to haunt this house since my death to atone for a dreadful deed that I committed. And only a maid like you can free me. Do you wish to help me!?"

The girl had lost the power of speech in her terror, and so she nodded timidly.

"You have a kind heart," sighed the knight, "Wait for me here tomorrow evening at the same hour, and I shall come and explain what you must do. But you must tell no-one of our meeting, or I shall not be released!" The armour clanked, the cold wind blew and the knight was gone. Half dead with fear the girl woke her mother and between her sobs told her what had happened. The mother comforted her daughter, put her to bed and waited until she was asleep. She had already decided that she would go to the meeting with the iron man instead of her child. The next evening she locked her daughter in her room and sat down in the kitchen herself. The hours went by until the clock struck midnight. The iron knight appeared in a blast of cold air. When he saw the mother instead of the daughter, he realised what had happened. "Another hundred years!" he sighed, and disappeared.

The house was pulled down long ago, but the tale of the iron knight is recalled by a statue by Ladislav Šaloun of a knight and girl on the building of the Prague City Authority at the corner of Mariánské Square and Platnéřská Street.

The Green Frog
U radnice 8

In the house with the beautiful stone frog on its façade there once lived a tailor called Lokýtek, together with the housekeeper who cleaned and cooked for him. Lokýtek was quite a good and handy tailor, but he had an excessive passion for conjurers and jugglers. Whenever new conjurers, artistes or jugglers came to Prague, Lokýtek was sure to be there in the front row, watching their acts, tricks and spells with open mouth. It happened one time that Lokýtek was down at the market place staring as the street performers swallowed swords, or stood on top of each other and then somersaulted down to the ground, tightrope walked and swallowed fire. Lokýtek was particularly entranced by one young man in a green suit. His body seemed to be made of rubber, and he could twine his arms and legs and head together in such an amazing way that there was no telling which was his front and which his back.

A few days later, when the city streets had emptied and people were sitting down to supper, the terrified housekeeper ran out of Lokýtek's house.

"Quick, help, someone!" she cried, shrieking and lamenting until the neighbours came running out of the adjacent houses. Quite a crowd of curious citizens had gathered around Lokýtek's house by the time the town guards arrived. The armed men soothed the housekeeper and their jaws dropped as they listened to her stuttering tale:

"Towards evening, my master was tinkering with something in the parlour. I ran into the kitchen around the stove to make sure the supper wasn't burning. Suddenly I heard strange noises, groaning and a scream. I hurried back to see if something had happened to the master. I opened the door, but he was nowhere to be seen, and on the seat where he'd been sitting there was a huge green frog! It must have gobbled him up!"

The bravest of the guards ventured inside the house with his sword drawn to ward off an attack. For a moment there was silence, and then the guard staggered out, doubled up with laughter. And behind him came the master tailor, safe and sound, but in a strange green costume. Somewhat unwillingly, he explained what had happened.

"I was at the market and saw a juggler in a green costume putting his legs behind his shoulders. So I ran myself up the same kind of costume and tried to do the same. I got my legs over my shoulders, but I couldn't get them back again. Then along came Maria and kicked up all this fuss about a frog!"

This story had all Prague laughing. When Master Lokýtek died, his neighbours had a great stone frog carved above the doors of his house in memory of the incident. And it still guards the house to this day.

The Severed Arm
Malá Štupartská 6

Inside the Church of St. James, to the right of the main entrance, a blackened human arm hangs upon a chain. A plaque beneath it tells a remarkable story. One night a thief hid in the church when the doors were locked. He had his eye on the precious jewels that adorned the miraculous statue of Our Lady on the altar, but when he reached for her pearl necklace the statue suddenly grabbed him by the arm. Its grip was so tight that he had no way of escaping, try as he might, and had to stay by the altar until morning when the verger found him. Help was summoned but to no avail, for nothing could pull the thief's arm free. In the end the executioner had to be called to cut the thief's arm off. The severed limb then fell of itself from the hand of Our Lady and it was hung up on the church wall as a warning to others. The culprit spent some years in prison, and when he was released, he begged the monks in the St. James' Monastery to take him in, so that he could atone for his sin by serving them. And rumour has it that they accepted him.

The Veil Given Twice for Love

The Carolinum, Ovocný trh 3 – 5

During the reign of the Emperor and King Charles IV, there lived in Prague a burgher called Rotlev. He owned a rich gold mine in Jilova, and so for many years he prospered and his wealth increased. But then the miners began to report that the veins of gold were dwindling. They tried to dig deeper and in different parts of the mine, but their picks struck only waste rock and not a grain of gold. Rotlev nonetheless believed that there was still enough of the precious metal somewhere in the mine, but alas, the months went by fruitlessly and little money was left for further prospecting. The burgher had to sell part of his property to pay the miners for another week and then another month of work. And the money kept vanishing without any gold appearing. Rotlev was downcast and worried, but was still sure there was more gold in the mine. He would lie in bed, sleepless, and the gold would hover before his eyes - great, glittering, cold veins of gold in cracked walls of rock.

One day it became clear that nothing short of a miracle would save Rotlev from beggary. The house had been mortgaged, the furnishings and valuable articles sold off. Rotlev had nothing left to sell.

"If only I could pay for just one more week of mining!" he said to his wife with a sigh. She loved her husband dearly, and was grieved by his suffering. She went into her parlour, opened her chest and took from it the last valuable object that remained in the house. It was a veil embroidered with gold, which her husband had given her as a wedding present. Rotlev was reluctant to accept the veil for he knew how much it meant to his wife. But she simply smiled and said,

"Sell it. Once you gave it me for love, and now I give it back to you for love. Even if you lose everything, there is no reason to despair when we love each other. We shall get through somehow!"

Tears came to Rotlev's eyes. He warmly embraced his wife, and hurried off with the veil to find a middleman.

Three days passed as the miners continued work. On the morning of the fourth day a messenger came to Rotlev from Jilova with the news that they had hit a golden vein in the mine. And no ordinary vein, for the deeper the miners dug, the more they found! Rotlev was saved. With the first money from the mined gold he bought his wife's wedding veil back from the middleman, and the new vein was so abundant that within a year Rotlev was even richer than he had been before. People began to call the lucrative mine "the Wedding Veil" after Rotlev's wife's loving gift. Rotlev had a grand house with a beautifully ornamented Gothic oriel built in the Old Town. Years later, King Wenceslas IV acquired it for Prague University, and, under the name of the Carolinum, it is still the seat of the university today.

The Ring inside the Fish
V kotcích

Long ago in Prague there lived a rich merchant woman. She traded in every possible commodity and owned several shops at V kotcích and other Prague marketplaces, and her fortune just kept growing, but she was as proud and miserly as she was clever.

One day, the lady was driving across Charles Bridge in her coach. A ragged woman who was sitting there begged her for alms but the lady dismissed her rudely. The beggar nodded her grey head and called after the coach, "You'll be sitting here yourself after a year, you mark my words!"

The lady heard her. She made the coachman stop, got out, pulled a precious ring off her finger and flung the ring over the stone balustrade into the Vltava. "Some people have good fortune, and others misfortune," she jeered triumphantly at the beggar, "My good fortune is as sure as the fact that this ring will never return to my hand!" Then she had the coachman whip the horses and she departed, pleased to have taught the impudent old woman a lesson.

Some time later the rich merchant woman was holding a grand banquet in her house. When baked fish were brought to the table, the lady began to carve one and her knife scraped on something. She was just about to shout a rebuke at the servants for failing to clean the fish properly, when she looked at her plate and saw - the ring.

The fish had swallowed it, fishermen had caught the fish, the maid had purchased it at the market and brought it to the kitchen. The lady immediately remembered the old beggar woman's prophecy and felt uneasy. And she was later to remember the ring more and more often, because from that moment on her luck turned and misfortune followed misfortune. First she lost a great deal of money in an unwise business venture, then her wagons full of goods were attacked and pillaged by robbers, and finally her house was struck by lightning and burned to the ground with all her property. Within a year she had lost everything. And there was nothing left for her to do but go to the bridge and beg for alms along with the other beggars.

The House At Death
Dlouhá 5

Where an Art Nouveau apartment house now stands in Dlouhá Street, there was once a house that belonged to a rich burgher. For a long time he had no children, but after many years his wife gave birth to a beautiful baby boy. The parents were overjoyed, but their happiness was to be short-lived, for when the boy was just a year old, he disappeared and was nowhere to be found. The stricken parents searched the whole house from attic to cellar, and the whole neighbourhood too, but in vain. The next day the neighbours' maid remembered that some vagrants had been passing through the street at around the time the boy went missing, and that one of them had been carrying a crying baby wrapped in rags in his arms. The guards at the town gates were immediately ordered to search anyone who looked suspicious, but it was too late. The vagrants were gone.

The years went by and the unfortunate parents remained alone, blessed with no more children. Then the burgher died. His widow was sad, alone in the great house; her days and nights went by monotonously in emptiness and grief for her husband. Then one day a stranger knocked at the door and asked for a roof, and the widow was glad to give him lodging. The young man rented a room from the widow and life in the house soon became more cheerful. The two would spend the evenings together, and the young man would tell the widow all about the foreign lands and cities he had visited and the books he was reading. Despite the great difference in their ages, after a while their friendship blossomed into love, and they married and lived as husband and wife, happy and content. The young man's only source of regret was that he could tell his wife nothing about his relatives. All he knew was that he had been brought up by some travelling people who had adopted him when he was a baby. It tormented him so much not knowing who he was and where he came from that one day he bade his wife farewell and went off to find the vagrants.

Knowing as he did the places where the tramps usually lingered in spring, where they went and where they spent the winter, he soon caught up with them. Immediately he told them the good luck he had encountered and expected them to share his joy, but they turned away from him in horror and refused to speak to him. Finally one white-haired old woman revealed to him that he had been kidnapped as a child from a burgher's house in Prague. They had wanted to get a ransom for him, but fearing punishment, they had taken him with them to foreign lands. When the old woman described the house, the young man's blood ran cold. It was the house where he now lived, and he had married his own mother. Miserable, he returned to Prague and told his wife, who didn't know whether to rejoice at the return of her lost son or to despair at the cruelty of fate. And because the truth can never be kept secret for long, soon the story got out and people started to mutter about the scandalous situation. At that time such a crime, even if unknowingly committed, was punishable by death, and the young man was sentenced to die. The punishment was carried out in front of the ill-fated house in Dlouhá Street, which from that time on was never known as anything but the 'House At Death'. Later an unknown artist painted a picture above the door showing a man kneeling with his head on the block and above him an executioner with a raised axe.

The Courageous Nun
Convent and Church of St. Anne, Anenské Square

The former Convent of St. Anne's with its church of the same name was originally the seat of the Knights Templar. After the Templar Order was dissolved, the complex was turned over to Dominican nuns. During the Hussite Wars, when an army led by Jan Žižka of Trocnov pillaged many monasteries and churches in Prague, St. Anne's was the only one spared. Legend has it that when Žižka arrived at the convent with his soldiers, the gate opened and out came an ancient nun. "Johnnie," she said to Žižka, a general who was feared throughout Europe, "Johnnie, don't you recognise me, your aunt? For the sake of our kinship, please spare this convent!"

"I will do as you wish, aunt," said Žižka, "but never ask me any other favours again in this life!"

Then he turned his horse and rode away with his troops.

Swallow's Water
The Convent of St Agnes, Anežská 12

The founder of St Agnes' Cloister was Agnes Přemyslovna, the youngest daughter of the Czech King Přemysl Otakar I. As a young girl, she renounced the worldly life and in 1231 she established a convent on the banks of the Vltava, at a spot known as na Františku. Agnes was an admirer of Clare of Asissi; she gave up worldly possessions following the example of St Francis of Asissi, and invited nuns of the order to her convent and became its first Mother Superior. The Poor Clares were devoted to poverty and charity, and so the poorest of the poor often sought shelter and assistance at their gates.

One day, an impoverished noblewoman from somewhere in Poland sought shelter at St. Agnes' Convent. Old and ill, she no longer had anyone in the world to care for her. The nuns took her in and allowed her to stay in the convent. In return, the grateful noblewoman gave them her secret recipe for a miraculous medicine that had been handed down from generation to generation in her family. When she died, the sisters continued to make the curative drops themselves and used them to cure many a sick pauper. The poor started to call the medicine "Swallow's Water" or "St Agnes' Drops".

When the convent was dissolved, the sisters left, taking the secret of swallow's water with them. One of them stayed behind, however, settled in Dlouhá Street and went on making the curative drops, which she distributed to the poor. But after she died, there was no-one left in Prague who knew how to prepare them. A few bottles remained with the old widow who had given the nun lodgings, and she hid them away like a precious treasure.

Some time later, a young student arrived at the widow's house. He said that he came from Poland, from the same family as the noblewoman who years before had found refuge in St. Agnes' Convent, and he also confided that she had been the only person who knew the secret of the medicine. The widow gave him one of the last bottles but could provide him with no further assistance. The student, however, was keen to persevere and tried to discover the secret of swallow's water by himself. He conducted all kinds of experiments on the liquid in an attempt to analyse it and ascertain its ingredients. Often he worked into the early hours of the morning.

One night there was suddenly a loud explosion from his room, and when the terrified widow rushed in, she found the student lying dead amid the burnt wreckage of the furniture. And so the secret of the miraculous medicine that had restored so many poor people to health was lost forever.

The Unfortunate Nun
St. Agnes' Convent, Anežská 12

Once a wealthy knight had his daughter confined in the convent as a punishment for disobeying his will and falling in love with a poor boy from the village below his castle. The boy soon discovered where the cruel father had hidden his beloved. He sent her a secret message telling her to slip out into the convent garden at night, where he would be waiting for her. Their meeting was ecstatic! Fortunate but alas unfortunate. After passionate kisses and embraces they planned an escape together, but one of the nuns, who had been unable to sleep and had looked down from her window into the garden, saw them together and reported it to the girl's father. On the appointed night when the two young people were to escape, the father was waiting in the shadow of the convent wall. After a while, the lovers appeared. The youth was holding the girl's modest bundle of belongings in one hand and helping her over the high wall with the other. The pair had no inkling that just as they thought they were free, they were in fact facing certain death. The girl's father hurtled out of the darkness with drawn sword and before the couple could grasp the situation he had thrust his sword into the youth's breast. "For God's sake, father, what have you done?" cried the girl, throwing herself on her beloved and loudly lamenting. Too late, for her beau's eyes were already extinguished and blood came from his lips. He was dead. But the knight in his fury lost all control. With his second blow he slew his own daughter. Only when it was all over and the two bloody bodies were lying at his feet did he cry out, in a voice of despair, "Wanton daughter, it is your fault that shame will fall on our whole line for so dreadful a deed! God knows, even after death you will find no rest while this convent still stands!" Then, sword in hand, he ran off into the darkness and was never seen again. The nuns buried the poor girl in the convent but could not undo the father's curse. And so her unhappy ghost walked the passages of the convent on dark nights, with heart-rending wails.

Years and decades passed, and the time came when the nuns were forced to leave St. Agnes' Convent. Moss grew over its silent walls, the empty churches loomed accusingly against the sky, and weeds overran the garden. Only the wind disturbed the desolation, sending the snowflakes whirling in winter and whispering in summer through the bent crowns of ancient trees.

A poor girl moved into a little house with a small window overlooking the convent garden. She was in love with a boy from the neighbourhood but his father was against the match, refusing to allow his son to wed a girl even poorer than himself. The girl suffered such pangs of frustrated love that one evening she decided it would be better to end her life. She made herself a lethal poison and, with the glass in her hand, she glanced out through the window into the convent garden where the wind was blowing the dry leaves around in the twilight. Her eyes were full of tears, and so it was at first only mistily that she perceived the figure in the grey habit hastening to her window. Suddenly, a gust of icy wind blew open the window, the grey figure seized the glass out of her hand, threw it far away into the garden and then vanished. Stunned, the terrified girl continued to stand at the open window for some time, and although the spectre had bewildered her, she knew now that she must live on.

Yet life is hard and sad. As the months went by, she still could not save the money that the father of her beloved demanded from

a bride. Winter, spring and summer passed, and autumn returned once more. One evening, she was standing as she had stood the year before, looking into the convent garden. Suddenly the same icy gust blew through the window, a grey figure threw a small purse into her lap and vanished into the darkness. When the girl opened the purse, she found exactly the amount of money she needed. Soon afterwards she married her young man, and they had plenty of children and lived happily. But she never forgot the ghost who had helped her - undoubtedly the spirit of that unfortunate nun who had never lived to be happy herself, but had given happiness to another.

The Three Standard-Bearers
Husova 12

In a house in Husova Street there once lived three soldiers. They were great friends, shared a room, and in the evenings they used to go out together to the Old Town taverns in search of girls. But they all served in different regiments, and when they were called to the war, they had to part company. On the evening before their departure, they went drinking together in a nearby tavern, ordered one pitcher of beer after another, sang noisy military songs and clapped one another on the shoulder, saying "When the war is over, we'll all meet here again!"

As dawn approached, the soldiers were the last guests in the tavern. The innkeeper was wiping the tables and sweeping up, but he knew the soldiers and he knew they were having a farewell party, and so he let them sit there for a little while longer. All three, however, had already drunk deep, their cheerful mood was gone and they were as wistful as only soldiers can be. Suddenly one of them said, "But I'll tell you one thing, brothers, let none of us be stupid enough to get himself killed in battle! It would make the other two sad if one of us was gone!"

"That's easy enough to say," remarked the second soldier, raising his head from the table where it was resting, "But how would the others even know if the third had already gone to meet his maker? Or the third, or the second or the first..." His thoughts were as confused as his tongue but his comrades understood him.

"I know how we'll do it!" the third exclaimed and struck the table with his palm so hard that the innkeeper gave them all a reproving look, "If one of us falls on the battlefield, he will come back here in the night like a ghost and tell the others about it! We'll shake hands on it!" As they made the promise they felt a chill, but they washed the black thought away with a last pitcher and went home. A few days later each of them was marching to a different front. Months went by, and two of the comrades came home safe and happy. But the third did not appear. Until one night, when the two were peacefully asleep in their beds, they were woken by the ghost of their dead companion. He floated into the room bathed in moonlight and sadly pointed to the bloody wound in his chest. "And within a year you will come after me," the spectre sighed, and vanished. The blood froze in the veins of his comrades, their hair stood on end and their teeth chattered. From that time on they were gripped with fear, and didn't even go to the tavern for they were always thinking of the words of their dead friend. To avoid the evil prophecy, they left the military profession and joined the nearby monastery of St. Giles. But it did them no good, for death still found them both their within the year. Perhaps the three met

41

in some heavenly tavern for a pitcher of beer. On the façade of the house where they lived there are three gilded metal plates bearing the portraits of the three standard-bearers.

The Gingerbread Heads
Karlova 3

On the corner of Karlova Street and Seminářská Street stands the House At the Golden Well. It took its name from a well in the house cellars, which was the subject of strange tales. People said that there was often a golden glow in the water, and that the light must certainly come from hidden treasure. Out of curiosity, one maid leaned so far down over the well that she fell in and drowned. The corpse was fished out of the well and the water pumped out so that the well could be cleaned, and the tale turned out to be true: a stone came loose from the side and fell away, and behind it came a shower of gold ducats. The owner of the house was overjoyed, but his happiness was spoiled by the ghost of the drowned maid, which walked the house every night, dripping wet and wailing.

Legend has it that she was not the only ghost in the House At the Golden Well. Apart from the sodden maid, its passages were haunted by the spirit of a knight and his lady, both headless. Nobody knew their story and so no-one knew how to set them free. Until a pastry cook came to live in the house; he baked plaited pastries small and large, sprinkled with sugar, poppy-seed and salt, rolls and cakes, but chiefly all kinds of gingerbread, which he decorated beautifully. He was honest and skilled, loved his trade and was always thinking of ways to improve his goods so that they would sell even better. Even the Old Town councillors bought his delicacies.

One evening he was rolling out his dough in a great trough as usual, and cutting out hearts, ponies, stars, soldiers and babies. As he put the first batch in the oven, he was wondering what other shapes he could add. He decided to make some figures of the ghosts, the knight and his lady, since he was sure they would go down well with customers! But because it occurred to him that no-one would want to buy figures without heads, he gave them heads of his own invention and went to bed. In the morning he had a most unpleasant surprise when he found that all the heads of the gingerbread knight and lady had been broken off and thrown on the floor. He called the maid and his assistants, but they swore they had done nothing, seen nothing and heard nothing. In the evening he baked new figures, and when he left he locked the kitchen and slipped the key into his pocket. Yet in the morning it was the same story as the previous day: the gingerbread knights and ladies were headless. The pastry cook couldn't make it out. He decided that on the third day he would sleep in the kitchen instead of his bed, and catch the impudent vandals who were destroying his work. He cut out his shapes, baked them and lay down to sleep on the floor.

He awoke suddenly in the night and saw the knight and his lady standing above him, both of them with heads. "You have made our gingerbread figures according to how we look," said the knight, "but our heads are of your own invention. We have therefore come so that you can copy our real heads. But hurry! Before the hour of ghosts is past, our heads must be back in the Vltava." The frightened pastry cook made the dough, cut out the figures and gave them heads that matched those of the ghosts. When he was finished, the knight examined the figures and said,

43

"You have done your work well. If you had botched it, you would now be a head shorter as punishment for wanting to make money from our misfortune. But now you may set us free, and moreover find great wealth. Many long years ago, we were murdered in this house when we wished to stay here for the night. The owner robbed us, killed us and dragged our bodies to the cellar. There he cut off our heads and threw them into the Vltava. Our bodies are buried in the cellar, and our money is hidden there as well. If you wish to set us free, you must dig up our bodies and bury them in the cemetery. If you do so, the treasure will come to you of itself." The pastry cook promised to do as he wished, and the spectres vanished.

The next day the pastry cook took a mattock and went down to the cellar. After some time digging up the floor, he found the bones of the unfortunate couple. He took them out, wrapped them in cloth and buried them in the cemetery. Shortly afterwards, the steps down to the cellar collapsed, taking with them part of the wall. Behind it was a niche containing a heap of golden coins. The pastry cook was happy, and the knight and his lady no longer haunted the house.

The Bridge of Eggs and Cream Cheese
Charles Bridge

In ancient times, before the first bridge was built across the
Vltava, wagons used to cross the river at a few places where it could
be forded. Many ferrymen plied their trade here as well. The old
chronicles have preserved the story of the great boat of the mythical
Prince Křesomysl of the ninth century, which ferried wagons and
people back and forth across the water in comfort. In the tenth
century, however, the first wooden bridge spanned the Vltava, and
in 1158 the first stone bridge was already standing. It was one of the
wonders of the world at that time, since at five hundred metres long
it was the longest in Central Europe. It was named after the wife of
Vladislav II, Judita, who had ordered its construction. To this day
you can see one arch of the Judita Bridge in the basement of the
Hospitaller Knights' Monastery on the Old Town Bank. But a great
flood in 1342 tore down the Judita Bridge. This was a huge calamity
for Prague and its trade, and so with great pomp the Emperor and
King Charles IV laid the foundation stone for a new bridge. He
made sure that the ceremony was carried out at a time precisely
stipulated as favourable by the court astronomer, who recorded it
numerically as 1-3-5-7-9-7- 5-3-1, i.e. in the year 1357, on the ninth day
of the seventh month at 5.31 in the morning.

Charles IV entrusted the construction of the bridge to the builder
of St. Vitus's Cathedral, Petr Parléř. To ensure that the bridge would

be not only imposing but strong too, the builder decided to add wine and raw eggs to the mortar, but there were not enough eggs for the task in all of Prague, and so they were brought from all corners of Bohemia by royal command. Wooden wagons lined with straw and laden with their fragile load in wicker baskets and trunks gathered on the bank of the Vltava, where the masons broke the eggs and mixed them with lime. Unfortunately, in the little town of Velvary the people misunderstood the royal instructions. Afraid that the eggs might break on the journey, they sent them hard-boiled. The inhabitants of Velvary became the laughing stock of Prague, and the joke has pursued them over the centuries. They were not the only ones to be ridiculed, however, for while the inhabitants of Unhoště transported their eggs properly, they were obviously unclear about the requirement for milk, which was used to thin the mortar for the bridge, and sent cream cheese as well.

All this means that Charles Bridge is probably the only bridge in the world to have been built not only of stone, but also of wine from the Prague vineyards, Bohemian eggs and the cream cheeses of Unhoště. This strange recipe seems to have worked, or Prague Bridge would not have endured for what is already six and a half centuries.

The Builder of Charles Bridge
Charles Bridge

Charles Bridge withstood all the great floods that struck Prague from time to time. But the legend runs that when the martyr priest St. John of Nepomuk was thrown from the bridge, one of its arches collapsed the very same day and no one could replace it, for whatever the masons had built by day fell down again during the night. One builder was determined to repair the bridge. He tried everything but without success until one night the devil appeared to him and offered him help. In return, the devil demanded the soul of the first person to cross the bridge after the repairs were completed. The builder agreed, but not wanting to have the soul of an innocent person on his conscience, he resolved to trick the devil.

After a few days, it was clear that the devil had kept his word. The work proceeded smoothly, and the arch was firm and held up. No-one was allowed to set foot on the bridge until the day of the ceremonial opening, and on the eve of that day the builder hid a cock in the Old Town Bridge Tower, with the aim of setting the bird free in the morning to cross the bridge first and so outwit the devil. Only the devil was even more cunning. He took on the shape of a building assistant, and as soon as the builder left his house in the Lesser Town early in the morning, he ran breathlessly up to the builder's wife and called to her to run to the bridge because an accident had befallen her husband on the other side. At the Lesser Town Tower, the guard knew the builder's wife and let her through.

When the builder on the Old Town Bank saw his wife running across the bridge, his blood ran cold. He realised that the devil had won, and taken the soul of the person dearest to him. What had been done could not be undone. The next night the builder's wife died, and with her the child she was expecting. The story runs that from then on the soul of the child used to float above the bridge at night, and solitary pedestrians hurrying across the bridge could sometimes hear it sneezing. Until a simple countrymen heard the sneeze and as was the custom, said "God bless you!" although no-one was to be seen. Then he heard someone answering in a thin voice, "God willing!" Only then was the little soul set free and able to fly up to heaven.

Bruncvík
Charles Bridge

The thirty statues of saints you see on Charles Bridge were not erected there until the mid-eighteenth century. These works were commissioned to adorn the bridge by noblemen, the church, the Prague Corporation and the universities. Their authors were leading sculptors of the day, and most are the work of Matyáš Braun, Jana Brokoff and Brokoff's sons. For centuries now Praguers have been teasing foreigners with the question, "How many statues are there on Charles Bridge?" It is a trick question, because in fact there are not thirty, but thirty-one statues. The thirty-first is the figure of Bruncvík with a golden sword, which stands on a bridge pier above the Kampa Park. It also used to be known as Roland, after the popular hero of Medieval chivalric legends recounted throughout Europe. Similar columns topped with a knight exist in other European cities, where they were originally raised as a sign of the jurisdiction of the city corporations. Unlike these other knights, however, Bruncvík on Charles Bridge has a lion crouching at his feet, and from there it was but a short step to the legend of how the dauntless Prince Bruncvík won the image of the lion for the coat-of-arms of the Kingdom of Bohemia.

The story goes that in olden times a Prince Štilfríd ruled the Bohemian Lands. His coat-of-arms was an ordinary iron cauldron, and longing for a more elevated emblem, he left his realm and through his courage in the service of the King of Naples he obtained a coat-of-arms with a black eagle on a field of gold. His son, Bruncvík, who became ruler of the Bohemian Lands after his father's death, resolved to add some even nobler emblem to his arms. He set out on his travels, journeyed through many strange lands, and then set sail. On his voyage he came to some wild rocky cliffs, where he spied a seven-headed dragon fighting with a lion. Seeing that the lion was getting the worst of the struggle, he joined in on the lion's side and slew the dragon. The grateful lion then accompanied him on his travels. In the realm of King Olibrius, Bruncvík also obtained a magic sword, which he then used to defeat every enemy. As soon as he said, "Heads down all!" the heads of his enemies would be rolling in the dust. With his miraculous sword and his lion at his side, the brave Bruncvík returned to Prague and proclaimed a silver lion on a red field to be the new emblem of the Kingdom of Bohemia.

It is said that Bruncvík's magic sword is walled up in somewhere in one of the piers of Charles Bridge. When the Bohemian Lands are in their greatest peril and misery, the knights sleeping in the Mountain of Blaník will awake and come to the aid of Prague. They will be led by St. Wenceslas on a white horse, and when he crosses Charles Bridge with his troop, his horse will stumble and the miraculous sword will jump from the ground straight into the prince's hand. The knights of Blaník will then effortlessly defeat the enemy, and peace and prosperity will return to the Bohemian Lands.

The Treasure in the Bridge
Charles Bridge

In an-out-of-the-way hamlet not far from Prague there once lived a poor peasant. His cottage was small, with a garden just as small and an apple tree, and he had many children, and being poor, they often wanted for food. One night he had a dream. He dreamt he was walking across Charles Bridge and suddenly stumbled upon a heap of gold coins. But then he woke and the coins were gone and the cottage as poor as before. Yet he had the same dream the next night, and the third. He could no longer ignore it, and he set off for Prague and Charles Bridge.

He walked back and forth on the bridge all day until evening, but could see nothing unusual. In the end a soldier who was on guard in a sentry box on the bridge asked him what on earth he was doing.

"How odd," said the soldier when the peasant had recounted his tale, "I too have had a strange dream, and also three nights in a row. I dreamt that a little way from Prague there was a village where there was a cottage, and in the cottage garden there grew an apple tree, and concealed in the roots of the tree was a golden treasure trove."

"But that's my cottage!" The peasant exclaimed.

Together with the soldier he hastened home, dug up the apple tree and under its roots he found the golden treasure. The two divided it fairly and both lived happily ever after.

King Wenceslas and the Bath Attendant Zuzana

Karlovy lázně – Charles' Baths, Smetanovo nábřeží 198

King Wenceslas IV was on bad terms with his nobles. They kept complaining that he filled the royal offices with his personal favourites and ignored their own proposals and advice. Quarrels and disputes multiplied until finally the nobles attacked the king on his way from the Castle of Žebrák to Prague and took him prisoner. They carried him off to the Old Town and threw him in prison in the Old Town Hall, from which there was no escape. He was kept under careful guard day and night. When the king was in his fourth month of imprisonment, he began to lose hope that he would ever be free again.

One hot summer's day, the king asked his captors to permit him to visit the city baths by Charles Bridge. They allowed it, but for safety sent four guards: one to stay at the door, one to watch his clothes, and two to go into the baths with him. After bathing, the king came out onto the stone courtyard gallery, wrapped only in bathing linen. It was a beautiful summer day, the sun shone in a sky so cloudless that it too looked freshly bathed, the birds chirruped and carefree people hurried across Charles Bridge about their business. Wenceslas wept at all this beauty, the beauty of liberty, the birds who could fly where they wished and even the beggar who could wander wherever he liked. The king alone – he only – was bereft of freedom. Wenceslas gazed sadly across the river to Prague Castle. It was so near, and yet he had no way of reaching his faithful followers. Looking down at the bank, he saw a small boat tied up under the gallery. Just at that moment, the young bath attendant who had served him as he bathed came onto the gallery. The king beckoned her to come closer, and quietly asked her to tell him her name. The girl recognised him, curtsied and said, "They call me Zuzana, Sire, and I shall do anything you wish."

"Do you see that little boat, Zuzana?" the king pointed at the bank. When the girl nodded he whispered, "Take me in it to the opposite bank. If you do it, you will never lack anything to the end of your days!"

The girl thought for a while. Then she gathered up the linen that was drying on the gallery and skilfully tied the pieces together with strong knots. Both of them climbed down from the courtyard. Zuzana untied the boat, the king sat down in it, and she quickly rowed over to thick bushes on the other side. When after a while the guards came out onto the gallery, a great surprise was awaiting them. They sounded the alarm and roused the whole neighbour-hood, but the king and Zuzana were already safe on the other side, hidden in the bushes. After the commotion in the baths had died down and as dusk was falling, they set out upstream through the rushes and found another boat, in which Zuzana took the king close to Kunratice, where Wenceslas often hunted and where he knew the woods well. By the light of the moon they safely reached the edge of Kunratice Forest, and the king's new castle (Nový Hrad). The burgrave immediately recognised the king, sorry as his state now was, and received both with sincere joy and appropriate honour. When they were sitting wrapped in warm blankets in the safety of the castle hall, the king called the treasurer and gave Zuzana a hundred gold pieces in payment.

"I know that your service merits more," said Wenceslas. "You did not fail me when my most faithful servants betrayed me. Give me a little time, and I shall give you greater recompense."

After a while, the King managed to resolve his disputes with the

53

Bohemian lords and regained all his royal power. Then he repaid the bath attendant in true royal style, by having the old baths by Charles Bridge demolished, building new ones and giving them to her with even more money. Nor did he forget her trade, which until then had been among the lowest of the guilds. He issued a charter raising the guild of barbers and bath attendants to the status of honoured crafts, and allowed them to use a new coat-of-arms – a towel rolled into a circle and inside it a kingfisher on a golden field, which was King Wenceslas's personal emblem. And so that people should never forget the brave and loyal Zuzana, the king had her portrait painted into a vault of the Old Town BridgeTower, where it can still be seen to this day.

A Forgotten Treasure Trove
The Clementinum, Křižovnická 2

After Prague Castle, the Clementinum is the city's second largest complex of buildings, including six courtyards, two churches and two chapels. It was built in the second half of the sixteenth century by the rich Jesuit order. When Pope Clement XV dissolved the Jesuit order in 1773, the Jesuits had to leave the

Clementinum, but many people believed that they would soon return to Prague.

In those days, a poor bricklayer was living in a small house by the Vltava. One evening, two men knocked at his door. They were clad from head to toe in black clothes and cloaks, with their hats pulled down low over their brows, and they asked him whether he would like to earn some good money. The bricklayer didn't much like the look of his visitors, but there was little work to be had and he had numerous children to feed, and so he agreed. The men told him to bring his bricklaying tools and get into their coach, since the work had to be completed by morning. In the coach one of the men tied a scarf over the bricklayer's eyes so that he wouldn't know where he was being taken, while the other cracked his whip and they set off. For a little while, the coach clattered on uneven paving, then slid along a muddy track, and then again scraped over stone. They were moving for a long time, and so the bricklayer had no way of guessing which part of the city they were in. Finally the coach stopped. The men led him into a house and then down a steep staircase somewhere into the cellars, where they took off the scarf. In front of him was a wall, and in it an opening into the next cellar that was just big enough for a man to get through.

"This wall needs bricking up. If you hurry, we'll make it worth your while," mumbled one of the men. Everything had been prepared, a heap of bricks and the mortar mixed, and so the bricklayer set to work. He couldn't help noticing that in the adjacent cellar there were stacks of heavy trunks piled on top of each other from the floor to the ceiling, and no door. Because he was skilled, he worked quickly. When he had finished, the men blindfolded him again, led him up from the cellar, seated him in the coach and set off again at a cracking pace. Before the first light of dawn, the bricklayer was back at his house. The masked men paid him five gold pieces. A very generous payment for such work, thought the surprised bricklayer.

"It is not just remuneration for the bricklaying," said one of the men as if reading his thoughts, "but for your silence too. If you let slip one word about what you were doing last night, you won't escape punishment!"

55

The easily earned money was warming the bricklayer's palm, and so he was happy to promise not to say anything to anyone. He was tired after his night's labours, went to bed and put the business out of his mind.

After a time, word spread around Prague that the Jesuits had been compelled to give up all their assets before their departure, but it had turned out to be much less than expected. There was also a rumour that they had hidden much of their gold and silver treasure in the walls of the Clementinum. When the bricklayer heard the tales, he immediately thought of his strange experience. Those mysterious strangers in the night must have been Jesuits, he thought, and they had driven the coach round and round just to confuse him! Losing no time, he secretly ventured into the cellars of the Clementinum to look for the bricked up hole. But although he went back there time and time again, he never found it. And so who knows? Perhaps the walled up treasure of the Jesuits is still waiting to be discovered in the Clementinum cellars to this day.

The Petrified Urchin
Church of St Martin's in the Wall, Martinská 8

The Church of St Martin's is one of the oldest in Prague. It was founded in the twelfth century and once actually stood in the Old Town city wall, as its name reminds us. Long ago, street urchins would often climb up on its roof and steal the young pigeons from their nests. One day a scallywag of this kind was sitting on a stone buttress just under the roof, fooling around and shouting at the other boys so loudly that a passer-by rebuked him. The boy just made a face, knowing that the gentleman in the black cloak was hardly going to climb up after him. The man stopped, turned his face up towards the boy, raised both arms and muttered something – and at that moment the boy turned to stone. He kneels there on the left buttress at the back of the church and grimaces down at us. And he never stops grimacing, the little rascal!

The Hairy Ghost
The Chapel of St Cross the Lesser, Karoliny Světlé

The oldest rotunda in Prague, the Chapel of St. Cross, stands at the corner of Konviktska and Karoliny Světlé Street and dates back to the end of the eleventh century. It is said that the vicinity was haunted by a monster all covered with fur, with long hair and a beard. Beside the chapel in Konviktská Street stands a small house, which once housed the night tavern 'U Jezurů' ('At the Lakes') where many girls of dubious reputation used to come to drink. The hairy ghost had some kind of grudge against them, for he would leap out at them from dark corners, jump on their backs and strangle them with long-clawed hands. Allegedly, he even bit off one poor girl's nose tip.

When the tavern closed, the hairy spectre was no longer to be seen near the rotunda. It was said he had been there to punish immorality so near to the holy place of St. Cross.

The Lesser Town

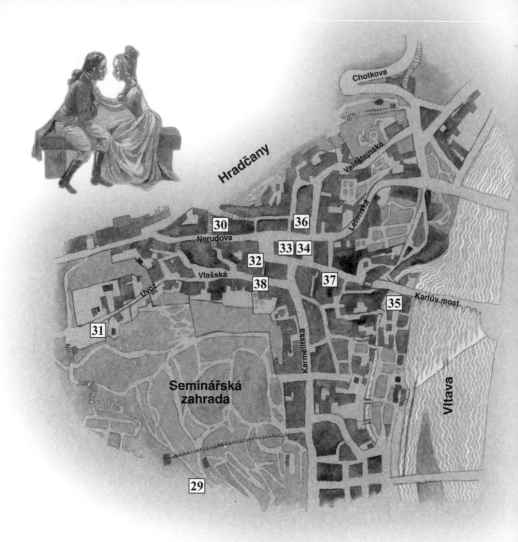

THE LESSER TOWN

The Hunger Wall
Petřín

One year during the reign of Charles IV, there was a terrible drought, the harvest failed and food was in short supply. Particularly in the towns the price of flour and bread rose so high that the poor could not afford them, and so many started to thieve and rob just to save their families from starvation. Soon the prisons of Prague were overflowing. When the Emperor Charles IV heard of the situation, he summoned the poor to Prague Castle, where he offered them great cauldrons of soup and fresh bread so that they could eat their fill. Then he appeared before then and said, "My officials will take you to a place where you will be given work. I shall not pay you in money, but you will receive clothing and food for your families."

The royal officials then led the people to Petřín Hill and showed them where they were to start building a new city wall to run from Strahov right down to the Vltava. The poor spent over two years building the long thick wall, which still stands today, and this work provided a livelihood for dozens of pauper families. People started to call it the Hunger Wall almost immediately, because of the toothed crenellations reminiscent of the teeth of the poor, who thanks to the wisdom of the emperor now had something to chew on.

True Love
Nové zámecké schody (The New Castle Steps)

You can get up to Prague Castle from the Lesser Town by two routes, either from Nerudova Street or by the New Castle Steps. The New Castle Steps end on the Hradčany Ramp, from which there is a superb view of Prague. Just above the steps stand three statues, among them a low column topped with a figurine of the Virgin Mary.

The Schwarzenberg Palace was once the home of a wealthy official. As is so often the case, while rich in possessions, he was poor in charity and kindness. He had just one daughter, called Alžběta, and unlike her father she abounded in goodness and beauty. It happened that Alžběta fell in love with an impecunious young man who lived with his mother in an attic room in Ostruhová Street. When evening fell the young people would meet under the statue of the Virgin Mary above the New Castle Steps, and then set off for the slopes of Petřín or wander hand in hand through the twilit alleyways of the Lesser Town. They were so alike in character that they might have seemed destined for each other, but fate was against them. They were divided by the huge gulf of property and the obstinacy of Alžběta's father. When his daughter told him about her suitor, he flew into a fury. "You want to choose penury? You expect me to give my daughter to some ragged, barefoot beggar so that he can waste my money? I shall never accept a pauper into my family!"

From that time on, the official constantly invited prospective grooms to the house, young and old, just so long as they had chests full of money, hoping that Alžběta would pick one. But she had eyes for none of them, and thought only of her beloved. Her father tried to persuade her with promises and threats, had her watched at every step and finally forbade her to leave the palace, but all to no avail. As soon as dusk fell, a light would shine briefly in the window of Alžběta's chamber and another light would shine immediately in the window of the young man's attic room in response. Then Alžběta would secretly creep out of the palace and run to the statue of the Virgin Mary and to her beloved. When Alžběta's father found out, he decided on a different strategy. He spoke with some other officials and arranged for his daughter's lover to be conscripted into the army.

And so the lovers met under the statue for the last time. Both had tears in their eyes, squeezed each other's hands and were in despair at the prospect of a long separation, as if they knew that it would last forever.

"I shall wait for you every day," Alžběta promised. "Every evening I shall look out of my window, until you give me a signal. As soon as the light flashes in your room, I shall come to our meeting place. So it will be as long as I live"

Early the next day, the young man went off with the soldiers to some foreign land and Alžběta never heard any news of him. From time to time, she took some money to his mother, but she too heard nothing from her son. The years went by and the boy's mother died. So too did Alžběta's father, and Alžběta had to move out of the palace. From her new lodgings she no longer had a view of the window of the attic room, and so every evening she would go to the statue of the Virgin Mary and look for the light from there. She stood there in summer and in winter, in rain and snow, in the heat and in the wind. Her hair turned silver, her face was etched with wrinkles, but Alžběta did not notice. She wore the same clothes that she had worn to meet her beloved, gazed with the same intensity at the attic window, and waited, waited and waited.

One frosty winter morning, the guards found an old woman,

frozen to death and covered with snow, under the statue of the Virgin Mary above the Castle Steps. Her face was like marble, and on her cheeks were two glittering tears of ice.

The Monk with his Head under his Arm
Úvoz

In one of the monasteries in the Lesser Town there once lived a monk who passionately loved playing dice. After dark he would sneak out of his cell, run to the nearest tavern and play there until dawn, when he would secretly slip back into his monastery. One cold damp night, a poor man, wet through with rain, sought him out in a tavern on Pohořelec. The man begged him to come and give the last rites to his dying brother, but the monk had just been losing and was burning with impatience to make good his losses. He kept feverishly throwing the dice on the table, but while first one player was lucky, and then another, the monk had no luck at all. All the while the poor man was standing at the door, but after a time he summoned up the courage to go and pluck the monk by the sleeve, telling him that his brother was indeed at death's door. The monk just angrily shook him off, ordered another pitcher of beer and immersed himself in the game. It was only hours later that he remembered the poor man, crossly threw away the dice and asked where he was supposed to go. He mounted a horse in front of the inn and rode through the rainy night up the steep slope of Úvoz. Suddenly a light appeared in front of him and he heard sighing. The monk immediately guessed that it was the soul of the sick man, who had died without receiving the rites, and it was true. As the light flickered in front of the horse, the animal took fright, its hooves slipped on the wet pavement and the monk was thrown from the saddle. As he struck the ground, his head was severed by the impact. Ever since, the monk has wandered along Úvoz on rainy nights, astride a horse but with his head under his arm and sighing. No-one knows how to help him.

The Fiery Skeleton
Jánský vršek

Jánský vršek (or John Hill) takes its name from the Chapel of St John that once stood there. Later the chapel was demolished and new houses built on the plot and on the site of the graveyard around it. It is said that every Friday at midnight a black coach pulled by horses black as night rides out of one of the gates of the houses, and in the coach sits a fiery skeleton without a head. The coach rides around Jánský vršek with a tremendous clattering for a whole hour, and then sinks into the ground. The fiery skeleton is reputed to be

the soul of a sinner who found no rest after death, but since no-one knows how to set him free he will probably be riding around there forever.

The Remains of Prince Wenceslas
The Lesser Town Square

Three years after the murder of Prince Wenceslas in Stará Boleslav, the order was given for his body to be conveyed to Prague Castle for interment in the Church of St Vitus. The ox-drawn wagon reached Prague without difficulty, forded the Vltava and headed for the castle. In those days, a prison stood where the Lesser Town Square was later to be built, and the oxen suddenly stopped in front of the prison and would move not a step further, despite all the efforts of the driver. It occurred to someone that in his lifetime Prince Wenceslas had always taken great care to ensure that no-one should suffer injustice, and so if the oxen had halted before a prison, it must be because someone was incarcerated there unjustly. The three prisoners languishing there were led out, and indeed – as one of them stood before the wagon, the shackles dropped from his arms and legs of their own accord. At that moment the oxen moved and the wagon with them. Everyone wondered at the miracle, and when a judge reviewed the man's case, he was found to be innocent. On the site of the prison, the people then built a Chapel of St. Wenceslas, which was torn down centuries later to make way for the Church of St. Nicholas.

The Inquisitive Jesuit
Church of St Nicholas, Malostranské náměstí 25

The builders of the superb Church of St. Nicholas and the adjoining monastic house were Jesuits. Their order was rich and powerful, and so they could afford to engage the best architects and artists of their day for the construction of the church. The main church vault is adorned with a huge painting representing the patron saint of merchants, St. Nicholas, above a quayside where merchants are unloading their goods. The painter the Jesuits approached was happy to accept the commission, but on one condition – that he should not be disturbed at all while painting. Perhaps he simply wanted to concentrate on an ambitious piece of work, or perhaps he wished to be free of any meddlesome onlookers all too keen to offer unwelcome comments and advice.

When the painter had been working for a long time, one inquisitive Jesuit could not control his curiosity and secretly slipped into the church. He hid behind a thick pillar, held his breath and watched the strokes of the painter's brush. But the painter on the scaffolding noticed a movement out of the corner of his eye, and because he was something of a wit, he pulled out a mirror, turned it so that it would reflect the inquisitive face, and with rapid strokes he sketched the monk's likeness onto the plaster. Then he turned and called down, "I can see perfectly well who's sneaked in here to watch! And the scoundrel will be punished for his curiosity!"

The monk was scared to death. He huddled still further behind the pillar, and when he thought that the painter was immersed in his work again, he carefully tiptoed out of the church. For weeks and weeks, he trembled at the thought that the painter would complain to his superiors and he would be punished. Nothing happened, however, and so the inquisitive Jesuit was relieved and decided that the painter had forgotten the whole incident. The day came when the painter had finished the work and all the members of the order gathered in the church to see the painting. They all gazed at it with admiration, until suddenly one of them called out, "Look, there's someone peeking out from behind that painted column there – and we all know that face!"

Everyone looked at the spot where the monk was pointing, and everyone recognised their colleague. He blushed scarlet and wished that the ground would open and swallow him up. Smiling, the painter explained how his face had got into the picture, and there was plenty of laughter, malicious and hearty. The inquisitive Jesuit stayed in the painting, and peeps out at visitors from behind the column to this day.

The Miraculous Painting
Na Kampě 9

Close to Charles Bridge on the Kampa stands a house with a picture of the Virgin Mary hanging on the façade, and on each side of the picture a wooden roller. The story goes that the painting was brought to the Kampa by water during a great flood. As the river rose, masses of wood, fragments of buildings and corpses of animals were washed up against the piers of the bridge, blocking the flow of the water so that it burst its banks and inundated the surrounding streets. It flowed around the houses in great eddies, even wilder than in its original channel. Praguers watched the flood from a safe distance and tried to help the people and animals caught up in the churning torrent. A piece of a wooden wall from some cottage, with a picture of the Virgin Mary still hanging from it, had caught in the crown of an uprooted floating tree. The owner of one of the houses on the Kampa was a very pious man who decided to save the painting. He took a small boat and embarked on the raging waters, almost lost his life, but eventually returned safely with the painting. They say that as soon as the painting had been brought to land, the water began to subside. The painting was then hung in a place of honour on the gable that faces Charles Bridge. According to legend, the Virgin Mary in the picture not only brought good fortune to the owner of the house, but always heard the prayers of others who turned to her in misfortune.

A poor village girl once served in the same house. She held the painting in great respect, adorned it with fresh flowers and took care

69

that the eternal flame beneath it should never go out. One day the girl was pressing linen on an old, heavy mangle. Her attention wandered for just a moment, and suddenly her hand was caught between the rollers of the heavy machine. In pain and fear the girl called out to the Virgin Mary to help her, and immediately the machine stopped of its own accord and the girl pulled out her hand unharmed. The owners of the house had two mangle rollers hung on each side of the picture to commemorate the miracle.

The Skeleton with a Nail in its Head
Tomášská

Many long years ago there lived a master locksmith in Tomášská Street in the Lesser Town. He had a pretty wife, was hard-working and understood his trade, and so he prospered. More and more custom came his way, and so he engaged a young journeyman to help him in his workshop. Before long, the sparrows on the slopes of Petřín were chirruping that there was something more than neighbourly friendship between the journeyman and the master's wife. But the locksmith suspected nothing, because he loved his wife

70

deeply and she could twist him round her little finger. He had no idea that the two lovers met secretly at night and were plotting how best to get rid of him.

One morning, the wife ran out of the house weeping and crying that her husband had suddenly died in his sleep. She mourned him, gave him a fitting funeral and wore black for some time. The neighbours felt sorry for the young widow, and so it did not strike them as odd that before the year was out she was celebrating her marriage to the young journeyman. After all, a workshop could not be long without a master, or a woman without a man.

A few months after the wedding, however, word spread among the neighbours that strange things were happening at night in the locksmith's shop. Some of them had seen the dead man walking about the house and heard him lamenting. But who could believe such ridiculous tittle-tattle!? The newly weds were living a happy, respectable life and the former journeyman plied his trade as honestly as his master. Seven years passed by. At that time, there was a rule that after seven years, old graves in the cemeteries were dug up and the coffins moved. And so it happened that the master locksmith's grave was opened, and as soon as the rotting coffin fell apart under the blows of a picket, the sexton saw that the corpse had a long rusty nail stuck in its skull. The locksmith had possessed thick hair, and so at the funeral no-one had noticed the nail. The sexton reported his discovery to the authorities, and when the guard came for the master's former wife and her husband, they were unable to deny their guilt for long. The judge sentenced them both to death, but the wretched locksmith found no rest even after his murderers had been punished. His ghost is still said to walk the neighbourhood at night, in the form of a skeleton with a nail in its head. Perhaps he would be set free if someone pulled the rusting nail out of his skull, but no-one has been brave enough to try.

The Bell that Announced Misfortune
Mostecká 14

In Mostecká Street not far from Charles Bridge stands the House At the Three Bells. When it was built more than three hundred years ago, the workmen digging the foundations found three small bells in the ground. Long ago the bells had hung in the tower of the Episcopal Palace that had once stood on the site. The owner kept the bells as valuable mementoes and when the house was finished, he hung them in a small tower in the courtyard. One of the bells was white and this was used to call the servants to lunch, the second was red and rung as a summons to evening prayers. The third, the black bell, was sounded when someone in the house died.

One day, the owner of the house left on a long journey and his wife stayed at home alone. Suddenly the black passing bell rang all by itself. Alarmed, the lady looked for the keys to the tower, but they were in their place and none of the servants had entered the bell-tower. It was a bad omen. Hardly had the bell fallen silent than a messenger was hammering on the door bringing sad news – the lord had met with an accident on the journey and perished.

Soon after the widow had buried her husband, suitors began to present themselves at her door. The lady could not forget her husband, however, and so she rejected all her admirers and would not even hear of remarrying. For a long time she lived alone, but then

72

grief and solitude began to weigh heavily on her. And at that time a new suitor began to court her, a foreigner and merchant who plied her with gifts and sweet words until she fell head over heels in love with him. She herself proposed that they marry, although everyone tried to dissuade her from this rash step, for after all no-one knew her intended groom and no-one knew anything about him, not even she herself. But the lady had set her heart on the match. She convinced herself that they simply envied her, and rejected her friends and their well-meant advice. And so the next summer a wedding took place at the House At the Three Bells. The feast was laid out in the courtyard, delicacies heaped on the tables, the music played merrily and the wine flowed freely. Late in the evening when the guests were about to depart, the groom rose with his goblet in his hand to propose a last toast to his bride. He was just opening his lips to speak, when the black passing bell rang out. It called with its metal voice, lamenting just as plaintively as when it had announced the death of the lady's first husband. The groom went pale, staggered, and fell dead to the ground with his goblet still in his hand.

When the lady had buried her second husband without having experienced a single day of married bliss, a great surprise awaited her. The day after the funeral the town guard banged at the gate, for they had come for her husband. He had been an impostor and a thief, and if he had not already died by that quirk of fate, he would certainly have faced the gallows for his crimes. From that day forward the lady had no ears for any other suitors, and she gave the black bell together with the others to the Church of St Lawrence on Petřín Hill.

Beautiful Laura with No Head
Karmelitská 2 – 4

The Church of St. Mary Magdalene and a convent of Magdalene nuns, dissolved in the eighteenth century, once stood in Karmelitská Street. When the nuns had gone, all kinds of people lodged in the convent. Wayfarers stayed there overnight, as well as poor countrymen and travelling players performing in Prague. When the actors came, they filled the convent with good cheer. The long corridors would echo with their shouts, their colourful costumes and gowns would be hanging everywhere, and singing, quarrels or passionate conversations could be heard from various corners as the actors rehearsed their roles. It was busiest here late at night after the performance. Admirers and suitors would gather at the doors, so that they might catch just a glimpse of the beautiful Laura. And the actress Laura was truly beautiful. Her black eyes glowed in her delicate face, her hair fell down to her waist like a dark waterfall, and when she smiled, every man's heart would catch in his throat. Laura's husband was also an actor, and he had no need to teach himself how to play jealous men for he guarded his wife from the others as a miser guards his treasure. He never moved from her side, watched her constantly, and whenever anyone began to make eyes at her he would scowl at the suitor and furiously drive him away. Laura was not allowed to speak even a word or accept any gift or bouquet.

Yet the more jealously he guarded Laura, the more her love for him withered. And just at this time a new admirer appeared in the shape of a handsome young count. He would go to every performance, was always sitting in the front row long before the play began, and when Laura came on stage he never took his eyes off her. He would wait for her in front of the theatre so that he could at least see her from afar, and would send her precious jewels and baskets of flowers. But Laura's husband was always at her heels and the count was a thorn in his side. He was already looking forward to leaving Prague for the next engagement and having his wife entirely to himself again.

On the eve of their departure he escorted Laura home from the theatre and then slipped out again for a moment to take leave of his friends. On his way back he met Laura on the stairs. She was coming down slowly, wearing a new gown of fine silk, a pearl necklace around her neck, and when she raised her hand with her fan, slender gold bracelets that he had never seen before clinked at her wrist. She was as exquisite as a dream, and she looked at him with a mysterious smile, but when she saw the expression on his face the smile died on her lips. Her husband caught her roughly by the waist and led her back to her room. Then the key turned in the lock and nobody saw either of them again that evening.

In the morning, everything was ready for departure, but there was no sign of Laura and her husband. The actors knocked on the door, and called, but no-one answered. When they finally broke the door down, they found Laura's body lying in a pool of blood, headless. Later that day the head, wrapped in a torn curtain, was delivered to the young count. Laura's husband had disappeared without a trace.

They say that on dark nights headless Laura appears in the former convent. She walks quietly through the shadowy corridors, and only the rustle of silk and the clink of her slender gold bracelets reveals where she is going. It is said that she will wander here unhappily until someone returns her lost head.

Hradčany

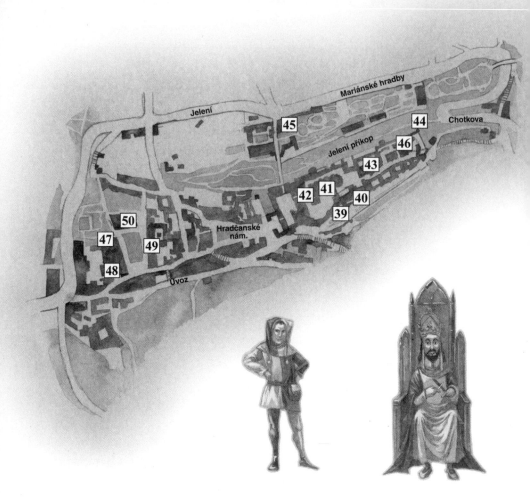

HRADČANY

Žito the Magician
Prague Castle

King Wenceslas IV was fond of merriment, but no-one could make him laugh like his court magician Žito. The magician had a justifiable grudge against the royal jester, who was jealous of the favour he enjoyed with the king and slandered him behind his back. The story goes that once at a banquet Žito transformed the jester's hands into horse hooves, and when everyone had laughed their fill, turned them into oxen hooves. Only when the jester had started to weep and wail heart-rendingly did Žito change his hands back into human form.

One day, King Wenceslas wanted to go for a ride. His coach was already waiting in the courtyard, but there was no sign of Žito even though he had been ordered to go with the king. The magician appeared only at the last minute with a terrible scraping and crowing – on a wagon drawn by three black cocks! The king nearly fell from his coach laughing and allowed the magician to accompany him through Prague in his strange vehicle.

Another time, Žito took thirty sheaves of corn and transformed them into thirty beautiful fat swine. He then drove the swine to sell at the market but on the way he met a buyer, the stingy baker Míchal. They quickly agreed on a sale but Žito warned the baker, "Just remember that my pigs must never be bathed!" The baker, however, had his own ideas, shrugged off the advice and immediately drove the swine to the ford. Scarcely had the creatures touched the water when they changed back into sheaves of corn. The furious Míchal immediately set off in search of the magician. There was no sign of him at the castle or in the market, but eventually Míchal discovered him sleeping in an inn. Yet however violently Míchal yelled and cursed, Žito would not wake up. In his anger, the baker caught Žito by the leg and tried to shake him awake, but the leg came away in his hand! Žito opened his eyes in an instant and started to lament and scream that now the baker must pay him handsomely for the loss of his leg. What could the baker do? The inn was full of witnesses and so he had no choice but to beg Žito's forgiveness and pay a fine sum of money for the leg. Žito stuffed the money into his pouch, touched the severed leg and, as if by a miracle, it grew back onto his body again. He jumped to his feet briskly, walked out of the inn with a laugh and didn't even look back at the woebegone baker.

Once the Duke of Bavaria was invited to the royal court as a guest and brought with him his own jugglers as a contribution to the merriment. They were excellent jugglers, and King Wenceslas and the whole court were amazed at their clever tricks. When the performance was over, the king summoned Žito to demonstrate his own arts, but whatever Žito came up with, even the most skilful turn, the German jugglers managed to repeat it after him. Žito was completely unable to outdo them. It made the magician sullen, and the king frowned too. The next day, when the Bavarian jugglers were performing again in the courtyard before the king and hundreds of amazed Praguers, Žito was not to be found anywhere. People began to think he must be ashamed because he couldn't accomplish anything to rival the Germans. Suddenly Žito appeared with two assistants and strode straight onto the podium. There he stopped, waited for the crowd to fall silent, rolled up his sleeves and, with both hands, started to pull at his mouth until it was stretched incredibly wide. The people held their breaths, not knowing what would come next. All at once the assistants grabbed one of the German jugglers and held him fast. The magician opened his mouth now as huge as an oven and swallowed the German! The audience applauded thunderously and collapsed with laughter, but that was not all. The assistants brought in a keg full of water and

Žito spat the Bavarian juggler out into it. The crowd roared madly, King Wenceslas praised Žito before them all, and the Bavarian conjurers returned home abashed and embarrassed.

Paleček (Little Thumb)
Prague Castle

In the Middle Ages it was the custom for every royal court to have at least one jester to amuse the king and his courtiers. Jesters were no fools, for they had to be clever, skilful and eloquent, and of course have an excellent sense of humour. King George of Poděbrady was no exception and had his favourite jester, Paleček, which means Little Thumb, a nickname given to him on account of his short stature. Paleček was merry, just and sympathetic towards the poor. People loved him and recounted tales of his escapades throughout the land.

Among the courtiers, however, there were murmurings that Paleček was conceited and excessively fond of new clothes, for look how he appeared in a new tunic and jacket several times a year! Yet these slanders missed the mark and there was quite a different explanation. After Paleček had received a new outfit from the king for the first time, he met a poor man, gave him his apparel and ran back to the king, saying, "Brother King, give me new clothes because I have just given mine to the Lord God!"

81

"How curious, and where exactly did you meet this Lord God of yours, and what did he look like?" asked the king with a laugh.

"It doesn't matter who exactly he was, but he was poor and needed new clothes. Is it not written that God says, whatsoever you do unto the poor, you do to me? So I have actually given my clothes to the Lord God." The king nodded and acknowledged that Paleček was right. He ordered new garments to be brought to the jester, and did the same whenever Paleček asked him.

In fine weather Paleček liked to leave the city and travel through the neighbouring villages. People were pleased to see him, because he always behaved as if he were quite at home and he would help them with their work whenever they needed it. But as soon as it was time for a meal, Paleček would vanish from the poor cottages and sneak into the kitchen of some rich man. He never went away hungry, but sometimes a rich man would at first object vehemently, "Brother Paleček, you want to eat with us, but you have done nothing for us. Why don't you eat with those for whom you have been working?"

Paleček would answer, "Believe me, brother, when you are poor I shall help you, and when the poor are as rich as you, I shall go and sup with them!"

Once a great feast was held at the royal feast in honour of noble visitors. Paleček sat down at the table right at the back by the door, where the least noble and least wealthy guests were seated. When the servants brought in fish on great platters, they served the king with the best pike and pike-perch, but put only small whitefish on the table behind by the door. Paleček didn't bat an eyelid. He took the smallest baked fish, put it to his ear and asked it, "Would you happen to know anything of my brother, by chance?"

He listened for a moment, than shook his head sadly, put the fish back on the plate, took another one and asked it the same question. People at the adjacent tables soon noticed the jester's strange behaviour. Some laughed and others expressed astonishment, until the king himself noticed the disturbance and had the jester summoned to speak with him. Paleček hastened to the king, his face grave and his brow furrowed.

"What on earth are you up to now, Paleček?" the king asked.

"Brother King, it is like this. I once had a brother who was a fisherman. Years ago he was drowned and I never heard any more of him, so I'm at least asking these fish if they have any news."

"And have they told you anything?" enquired the king, who already sensed a joke in the air.

"Alas no, Brother King. These fish on our table say they're still too small and young to know anything about my brother, but apparently their sisters on your table are much bigger and remember more, and so they may well have something to report". The king burst out laughing and ordered the biggest fish to be taken to the table by the door.

Such was the jester Paleček. Clever and wise, reminding the king through jokes and in all seriousness that his vocation was justice and compassion for those who did not live in wealth and luxury. When Paleček eventually died, they say that the king missed him so much that he soon followed his jester to the grave.

The Bell at St. Vitus's Cathedral

The Cathedral of St. Vitus, St. Wenceslas and St. Vojtěch, Prague Castle.

The Tower of St. Vitus's Cathedral is 99 metres high, and so the highest of all the historic towers in Prague. It contains the largest bell in Bohemia, which is known as Zikmund and is two metres high and weighs 18 tons. Sixteen pairs of horses were needed to convey the bell by special wagon to the Castle, but when attempts were made to hang it on a rope and pull it up into the tower, its weight snapped even the thickest ropes like fine thread. The king was annoyed. What was the point of a bell that could not be hung in a tower? But when his daughter saw it, she said, "Leave it to me, Papa. Wait and see, and in a few days the bell will be ringing in the tower of St. Vitus!"

The king was happy to entrust her with the task, and curious as to how she would manage it. His daughter was educated and clever, and had often out-argued the best scholars at the court in learned debates. The princess summoned all her women friends and shut herself up with them in her chamber. There they cut off each other's long hair and wove it into a strong rope with their nimble fingers. Meanwhile the princess sat over a piece of parchment and designed an ingenious mechanism that would safely lift the bell up into the tower. Carpenters and smiths made the peculiar machine according to her plan, and transported it to the forecourt.

On the appointed day, throngs of Praguers jostled under the tower of St Vitus, anxious to see what the princess had thought up. Many of them were very doubtful when they saw the slender rope woven out of hair, but when the bell was fastened to it and the machine clanked into action, the line tautened and the bell started to rise. It rose higher and higher, getting smaller and smaller in the eyes of the onlookers, until it had safely reached the edge of the scaffolding by the windows of the tower, where the workmen grasped it and heaved it inside. The courtyard resounded with applause and cheers, while the clever princess stood by the window, waving and smiling.

Reports of the miraculous machine soon spread throughout the country, and builders and apprentices came from over the border, wanting to know how it had been constructed. But the princess ordered the machine to be taken apart and then destroyed so that no-one would ever discover its secret.

The Miraculous Golden Lamp
The Cathedral of St. Vitus, St. Wenceslas and St. Vojtěch, Prague Castle

The superb tomb of St. John of Nepomuk in St Vitus's Cathedral is made of pure silver. Its rare ornaments include costly silver lamps. Legend has it that among them there was once also a lamp of gold. The goldsmith who had made it later fell into penury through no fault of his own and was likely to be thrown in gaol for debt.

Knowing no-one who could help him, he was in despair. One night he dreamt that St. John of Nepomuk appeared to him, and told him to go into the cathedral at night, take the gold lamp from the tomb, sell it and so pay off his debts. The goldsmith was an honest man and hesitated, but when he had the same dream for three nights running, he decided to obey the saint. He secretly slipped into the cathedral after dark, and hardly had he knelt at the saint's tomb to pray when the lamp itself floated down, lower and lower, until he held it in his hand. He then melted the lamp down in his workshop and used the gold to make beautiful jewellery that he sold without difficulty. He soon repaid his creditors and was no longer threatened with prison. Immediately he hastened to the cathedral to thank St. John of Nepomuk, but when he came to the tomb he couldn't believe his eyes. The golden lamp was hanging there as if nothing had happened.

The goldsmith did not forget the miracle that had saved him from prison. As soon as he recovered his prosperity, he made an even more beautiful golden lamp and went to hang it on the saint's tomb. The original gold lamp was suddenly nowhere to be seen. It had disappeared to make way for the new one.

How the Bells Tolled for Charles IV
The Old Royal Palace, Prague Castle

When the Emperor and King Charles IV was on his death bed in his palace on a November evening in 1378, Prague Castle and the whole town was silent and sunk in grief. All at once the bells of all the Prague towers rang out, and so did the passing bell in the tower of St. Vitus. At that moment the king breathed his last in his palace. At the sound of the death knell, the bell-ringer was astounded, for he had the key to the tower in his pocket. Breathless, he unlocked the door, ran up the stairs and saw the passing bell ringing of its own accord, unprompted by human hand, while the other bells accompanied it. It was the same in all the towers of Prague. They say it was Prague herself saying farewell to the emperor who had served her so well.

The Daliborka Tower

Golden Lane, Prague Castle

Today Prague Castle still gives the impression of a medieval fortress, especially if you look at it from Deer Ditch, which offers a good view of the elaborate Gothic fortifications built in the reign of King Vladislav Jagiellon in the fifteenth century. Here too stand the defensive towers known as Daliborka, the White Tower and Mihulka. When necessary, these towers also served as prisons, and in this respect the most famous of their cells and dungeons are those in the Daliborka Tower, named after its most celebrated captive, Dalibor of Kozojedy.

During the reign of Vladislav II there was great disorder in the country. The king had his seat in Hungary and only rarely visited Bohemia, so without the security of royal justice people resolved their disputes as best they could, some by violence and some by cunning. At that time the knight Adam Polskovský, known far and wide for his cruelty, was lord of the stronghold of Ploskovice near Litoměřice. He so oppressed his serfs that in the end the poor men revolted, took his castle by force and seized the knight Adam himself. Under threat of death they forced him to sign a proclamation releasing them from his domain and renouncing any intention of revenge. Then they withdrew and voluntarily became the serfs of the neighbouring knight Dalibor of Kozojedy, who was well-known for his just and mild nature. According to a different account, however, Dalibor had actually set his sights on his neighbour's lands and had deliberately incited the uprising, since in the end he had profited from it the most. But who can be sure now what the real story was? What is certain is that when news of the whole incident reached the royal governors, they sent the royal army to Poloskovice, returned Adam's property and threw the knight Dalibor into prison at Prague Castle.

Dalibor suffered greatly in his uncomfortable cell in the tower. In order to pass the time and divert himself from thoughts of his misfortune, he asked the gaoler to bring him a musical instrument. A few days later the gaoler brought him a violin. From morning to night the prisoner kept trying to play the instrument, holding the instrument one way or another, scraping the bow over the strings and at first producing only sounds like wailing cats. After a few days, however, he succeeded in producing clear, long notes, and his proficiency soon increased. As time went by Dalibor perfected his playing to such an extent that when he took the instrument in his hand, even the hardened gaolers and guards would weep at the beauty of the sound. Soon the news of his talent spread and many Praguers would come and stand under the tower each evening and listen to him play. They would put a little food, and sometimes coins or warm clothes into a basket that he let down from the window of his cell in the tower. Several young maidens in particular came regularly, listened to the sweet lament of Dalibor's violin, sighed and wiped the tears from their eyes, full of genuine pity for the young prisoner.

Until one day the crowd under the tower assembled fruitlessly, for there was only silence. When Dalibor's violin had failed to sound on the second and third day, people asked the gaoler what had happened to the knight. The gaoler just shook his head, confirming their sad suspicions. Fearing that the revolt of the Ploskovice serfs might serve as an example to others, the lords had sentenced Dalibor to death, and the sentence had been carried out in front of the prison early in the morning, while everyone was still asleep. The Praguers wept for their most beloved prisoner, and the tower was named after him.

But what was the real truth about Dalibor of Kozojedy's violin? In reality, the knight in the prison could never have played a violin, since the instrument only arrived in Bohemia a century after Dalibor's execution. And the Czech saying based on the tale, that "adversity taught Dalibor to fiddle", most likely originally meant that his sufferings under torture compelled him to confess.

The Lion Court
Jelení příkop/Deer Ditch

Monarchs and nobles often kept live heraldic beasts, like lions, birds of prey and of course horses, at their residences, and lions were kept at Prague Castle for centuries as the symbol of the royal emblem of Bohemia. Under Rudolf II, these wild beasts were given living quarters in what was known as the Lion Court in a corner of the royal garden. Apart from four lions and two lionesses, it was also home to a tiger, leopard and even an orang-utan, as well as many less exotic predators like wolves, foxes, lynx and wild cats. One day the emperor visited the enclosure with his entire court to show his bestiary to the envoy of the Turkish sultan. The envoy politely praised the zoo, and then stopped in front of the lion cage, glanced around at the young nobles of the imperial court and said with a smile, "In my country we also keep various wild beasts. And when my lord and ruler visits his lion court, one of the courtiers always asks him for permission to fight the lion. It is an old custom, but one through which his subjects express their loyalty and respect for the sultan."

The emperor understood the Turk's meaning. He gazed round at the fair faces of his retinue, but no-one seemed to have any desire to undertake a similar feat of heroism. They all looked down at the ground, coughed, or suddenly started up conversations with each other. But then the youngest knight suddenly stepped out from the throng of nobles, bowed to the emperor and asked permission to fight the lion. Pleased, the emperor gave his gracious consent. The keeper drove away the other creatures and left only the strongest and biggest lion in the cage. The knight took a light lance and bravely entered the cage.

The lion regarded him with its yellow eyes, crouched on the ground, lashed its tail and growled menacingly. Then it took a giant leap and only by a hairsbreadth did the knight move out of range of the lion's paws with their sharp claws. The knight immediately advanced, and before the lion could launch another attack, he threw his lance straight into the lion's heart. The lion got up on its haunches, roared in pain, and then his lifeless body fell to the ground.

The courtiers were generous with their praise for the knight's skill and courage, and the Turkish envoy himself expressed his admiration. The emperor Rudolf at once repaid the bravery of the young knight with a golden chain that he took from his own neck. Thus was the honour of Bohemian chivalry preserved.

The Chateau in Golden Lane

Zlatá ulička (Golden Lane), Prague Castle

Golden Lane is probably the most famous street in all of Prague. On one side the tiny houses are pressed to the wall, as if they would collapse at once without its support. Under Rudolf II these were the dwellings of the archers and their families. When Josef II dissolved the castle archers' corps at the end of the eighteenth century, the little houses were sold off cheap. Apart from the ordinary Prague poor, they became home to all kinds of eccentrics, fortune-tellers and soothsayers, who lent the alley an air of mystery. Artists and writers also fell under its spell, and, in 1917, Franz Kafka rented the house at number 22 as a study. And why was the alleyway called Zlatá (Golden)?. Legend has it that King Rudolf lodged his alchemists, and scientists here, because he had an obsessive longing to master the art of making gold.

Long afterwards a stranger moved into one of the smallest houses. This old man was a little eccentric, spoke with no-one and rarely went out of his humble abode. Yet he seemed to be engaged in some intense activity, for puffs of black, or yellow or even blue smoke often came from his chimney, and there was a light in his window long into the night. As the years went by the neighbours got used to the strange old man and decided that he was just a harmless lunatic.

But one afternoon the old man burst out of the little house, his eyes glowing, his long unkempt hair and beard flapping. He waved his arms above his head and cried, "Good people! I have done it, I have produced gold! Real gold!"

Everyone ran towards him, the old man gestured feverishly with his hands and began to stammer out an explanation, but suddenly he stiffened, pressed his hands to his chest and fell to the ground, dead. Because he had no family, the neighbours buried him in one of the mass paupers' graves. Officials entered the house. They found no trace of gold, but only a document identifying the dead man as coming from a famous and rich noble family. Soon the old man's son arrived in Golden Lane and asked the neighbours about his father's life there. What he told them in his turn was very revealing. Many years previously, the old man had lived peacefully with his children and their families in a great chateau in South Bohemia, but one day he had got it into his head that truly fairytale wealth might be obtained for his children, and had buried himself in books of alchemy and started to conduct all kinds of experiments in his chamber. The family feared that their father was becoming senile, and so kept trying to prevent him experimenting, but one day the old man disappeared. They searched all over Bohemia for him but found no clue as to his whereabouts. No-one suspected he had rented a house in Golden Lane in order to carry on with his experiments undisturbed. He left nothing to suggest he had really discovered the secret of gold, and if he had, he took it with him to the grave, but Golden Lane could now boast that at least one real nobleman had lived there. And by the time a good few years had passed since the old man's death, the neighbours never called the smallest house in Golden Lane anything but "The Chateau".

The Architect of the Černín Palace

The Černín Palace, Loretánské Square 5

The monumental, one-hundred-and-fifty-metre façade of the Černín Palace has adorned Loretánské Square since 1669. It was built for Humprecht Černín of Chudenice, the imperial envoy in Venice. The tale goes that for a long time the count failed to find an architect willing to attempt the grand and enormous palace he had in mind, but in the end one turned up of his own accord. The count liked his preliminary sketches, so he gave the architect a fat advance and work began immediately.

The architect had no reason to be sparing with the money the count had given him. He happily paid the wages of the labourers and craftsmen and the fees of the artists who adorned the palace with works of art. He was sure that the count would pay him the entire sum including his own fee as soon as the palace was ready. When the building was complete, the architect planned to go and see the count at his country residence, but on the eve of his departure he received news that the count had suddenly died. After the funeral the architect presented himself at the Countess's, submitted his accounts and asked for them to be paid. But the countess was appalled at the amount of money she was supposed to pay. She wanted to see a charter signed by the count and confirming the costs, but the architect did not possess one. He defended himself by explaining that he had relied on the promise of Count Černín, but without a contract or a bond, the countess refused to negotiate with him. The architect found himself in a hopeless situation. He was penniless, deep in debt, and had not been paid for the building.

In great despair he confided his woes in his brother, who happened to be a member of the secret society of the Masons. His brother took him to a secret Masonic gathering and asked the members of the brotherhood to help him. Those present listened to his story, consulted for a while among themselves, and then the Grand Master told the architect to have a contract drawn up as if the count were still alive.

The architect brought the contract to the next Masonic gathering. The Grand Master placed it on a small table at the far end of the hall, had all the candles put out and started a loud incantation in an unknown language. All at once, the figure of the dead Count Černín appeared in the darkness above the table. The count placed his right hand on the paper, on the spot left blank for his signature. Then he withdrew his hand and vanished. When the candles were relit, the terrified architect received his contract back from the Grand Master. In place of the count's signature he found the black print of a male hand, as if burnt into the document. "Show this contract to the Countess and you will see," said the Grand Master. The architect thanked him, hastened to the countess and showed her the document. When the countess looked at the contract, she grew pale. Then she summoned her treasurer and paid the architect all the money he had demanded, down to the last heller.

Slippers Made of Dough
The Černín Palace, Loretánské Square 5

They say that a proud and ostentatious countess once lived in the Černín Palace. Almost nothing was good enough or exotic enough for her. She had to have dresses made of gold and silver fabrics brought from the distant Orient, the rarest jewellery with precious stones, rose pearls and diamonds, slippers of snakeskin and the skin of birds, cloaks lined with the furs of arctic foxes and white ermine. But as soon as she had worn such rich and gorgeous robes and jewels once, she would cast them aside and never wear them a second time.

It so happened that her husband was planning a great ball. The most exalted guests were invited from near and far, the best musicians were hired, whole armfuls of flowers were ordered to adorn the ballroom, and whole wagonloads of the most select delicacies and rare wines were arriving at the palace. The countess, however, took no part in the preparations. She spent whole days lying in her canopied bed, bullying the maids and chambermaids. She had the most terrible problem: her dress of rose silk, light as a summer breeze, had already been made, but what slippers should she wear with it? All the best shoemakers in Prague were summoned in turn. They showed her the finest leather and materials of all colours, but none of it was good enough. Until one morning the countess woke, yawned, and glanced at the piece of fresh bread with butter and honey that the maid had brought her on a platter. "I've got it!" she cried, "I want slippers made of bread dough!"

She had the best master shoemaker called in and informed him of her wish. The shoemaker was appalled by such an impious idea. A poor family could have lived comfortably for a year for the price of a single one of the countess's rings, and a poor widow with children would have kissed her hand for a load of bread...while the proud countess wanted to walk on bread! But the spoilt countess would not be persuaded out of her whim. And so the baker baked a great loaf of bread, and the shoemaker modelled slippers from the soft crumb, decorated them with pearls and gold, and had them sent to the countess on a velvet pillow on the day of the ball. She was ecstatic. "Nobody can possibly have seen such slippers before!" she said to herself, and looked forward to being the centre of attention as always, admired because she possessed something that no-one else had.

And so it was. When she entered the hall, everyone gasped with astonishment at her dress and jewels, and when she told them about the slippers she was to dance in, they gaped even more. The ladies and lords loudly praised such an unprecedented idea, but many secretly thought that this time the countess had gone too far in her pride. The countess attracted the deepest bows and most florid tributes from an unknown cavalier, a dark stranger in expensive black clothing. She was very gratified by his flattery, and so danced almost every second dance with him in careless merriment. When the musicians announced the last piece of the evening, the dark foreigner steered her towards the door of the ballroom as they danced. When she showed alarm, he whispered, "I want to show you something unique, dear countess, something that only someone like you can appreciate!" The countess was reassured and the stranger danced her along the corridors further and further from the fading strains of the music and then down the stairs into the palace cellar. Suddenly suspicious, the countess now desired to tear herself away from him, but his black eyes flashed as he released his grasp and said quietly, "Look at your slippers!"

At that very moment flames leapt up from the bread slippers, burning the countess unbearably, and no matter how hard she tried she couldn't take the slippers off. Mad with pain and terror, she ran wildly through the labyrinth of dark cellar passages, wailing and screaming, but no-one could hear her through the thick walls. It is said that the proud countess is still wandering and wailing in the cellars of Černín Palace. And the dark cavalier? Who else could he have been but the devil?

The Loreto Bells
The Loreto, Loretánské Squareí 7

In the Nový svět (New World) district in Hradčany there once lived a widow who had exactly the same number of children as there were bells in the Loreto towers. The family was poor, but the widow was not cast down by their poverty, since her greatest riches were her beautiful children. All she could hide away against the worst of times was a purse of silver pennies. And one day, the worst of times came. Prague was struck by an epidemic of plague and every medicine was powerless against it.

The first to fall ill was the eldest boy, and the disease progressed all too fast. One morning, the boy lay down with a fever, and the next day, towards evening, he died. The unhappy widow took one little coin from the purse and took it to the Loreto, so that at least the largest bell should ring for her eldest as he left the world. Then another child sickened and soon died. A second penny went to the Loreto, and the second largest bell rang mournfully. The sickness struck down a third child, then a fourth.... Until the widow had buried all her children, and each had been accompanied out of the world by one of the Loreto bells. When the widow returned from the cemetery where she had buried her youngest daughter, she realised that she too was ill, but she had used up all her coins, and none was left for a bell to toll for her. She lay in a fever on her bed, and when she was about to draw her last breath, she heard all the Loreto bells chiming together. They were ringing of their own accord to accompany the poor mother on her last journey. And they say it was first time the bells chimed out the song they have sung ever since.

Drahomíra's Chasm
Loreto Square

Princess Drahomíra was the wife of Prince Vratislav, with whom she had two sons, Wenceslas and Boleslav. When Vratislav died, Drahomír became the regent because her first-born, Wenceslas, was still too young to rule. Wenceslas was brought up by Vratislav's mother, the pious Princess Ludmila, who was very popular among the people because she helped the poor, widows and orphans, nursed the sick and donated a great deal of her money to churches and monasteries. Drahomíra was jealous of Ludmila's popularity, and also disliked the way her mother-in-law was leading Wenceslas to piety. Drahomíra was a Christian too, of course, but it was rumoured that she still sacrificed to the pagan gods in private. From hatred it is but a short step to evil-doing. Drahomíra chose two armour-bearers from her retinue, Tunna and Gomon, paid them and sent them after Ludmila at Tetín, to rid the world of her mother-in-law once and for all. They performed their bloody duty, but the murder of the respected and beloved princess shook the people. Thereafter, Princess Drahomíra no longer commanded respect and people avoided her. She did not even give up her intrigues when the young Prince Wenceslas ascended the throne, for she turned Wenceslas's brother Boleslav against him, and it was Boleslav who later had the saintly Prince treacherously murdered at Stará Boleslav. It is said that from that time on Drahomíra could find no peace. She moved restlessly from castle to castle, but thoughts of her evil deeds pursued her everywhere. In the end, she made up her mind to leave Bohemia for ever.

Legend has it that early in the morning at Prague Castle she climbed into a wagon driven by her faithful servant. When the horse-drawn wagon was passing the spot where Loreto Square lies today, the bell in the tower of the small Cappuchin Chapel of St. Matthew rang out to summon the people to prayer. The pious servant stopped the horses and jumped down from the wagon to kneel and pray, but the princess called out angrily and ordered her to go on. All at once, the earth shook, there was a gigantic clap of thunder and a great chasm opened up in the ground. Drahomíra fell into its depths together with the wagon and horses. When the servant had recovered from her fright, she ran back to the castle and recounted what had happened. But no-one could be bothered to try to come to Drahomíra's aid. There was a bottomless abyss there for centuries afterwards, they say, and people steered clear of it. And it was rumoured that at night you could see flames springing from it, and hear the despairing shrieks of Princess Drahomíra, who had fallen straight into hell.

Josefov -
The Jewish Quarter

JOSEFOV – THE JEWISH QUARTER

The Oldest Synagogue in Prague
The Old New Synagogue, Červená 2

When the Jews came to Prague, the King assigned them a place on the right bank of the Vltava where they were permitted to settle. Before starting to build houses for their families, they conferred about how a synagogue might be constructed as quickly as possible. The arguments were endless, until a wise old man intervened. He told the others to start digging on a low hill nearby, saying that if they did so, they would see for themselves how to get a synagogue. The Jews obeyed him and set to work at once. They dug into the hill from the top and carried the earth to the bottom. When they had uncovered the upper part of the hill, they struck the top of a roof. Encouraged by the discovery, they redoubled their efforts and in just a few days they had uncovered the entire Old New Synagogue in the form that has been preserved to this day. Their joy was so great that they no longer wanted to keep on digging, and so the synagogue stands partially sunk into the ground. And it is said that it got its name from its strange rediscovery, for it was old yet new.

Another legend tells that angels brought the Old New Synagogue to the Prague Jews from their original homeland, Palestine.. The

103

angels strictly forbade the Jews ever to change it in any way, and perhaps there is something in the tale, because whenever the Jews tried to alter the building, something bad would always happen to put them off the idea. Consequently, the outside and inside of the synagogue have remained unchanged down the centuries.

The Rabbi and the Emperor
Široká Street

In the times of the Emperor Rudolf II the great Jewish man of learning Yehuda Löw ben Bezalel lived in Prague. He was famous for his wisdom and held in great esteem, which was why the Prague Jews elected him as their rabbi, teacher and leader. One day, however, the emperor decreed that all Jews must leave Prague. This caused great sorrow in the ghetto, for it is a terribly hard thing for people to leave their home, livelihood, the graves of kin, and trek out into the world to seek a new refuge. The rabbi immediately went to the palace to try and dissuade the emperor, but the guards had orders not to admit him. The rabbi considered how he might get a chance to speak to the emperor and decided to wait on Charles Bridge, for the emperor frequently rode out there on excursions. When Rudolf's coach approached, the rabbi raised his arm and stood directly in its path. The horses stopped in front of the rabbi as if commanded, and refused to move from the spot. The emperor's armed retinue ran up with swords drawn, but in front of the rabbi they were suddenly rooted to the ground, unable to take another step. Passers-by abused the rabbi, shouted at him to stand aside and started to throw stones at him, but as soon as the stones touched the rabbi they turned into beautiful bright blossoms. By now the curious emperor was leaning out of the window of his coach, and the rabbi was able to address him. The emperor listened to his plea and promised to visit him the next day at his house in the Jewish Quarter. The rabbi thanked him, bowed reverently and withdrew from the road. The coach rattled on and the armed retainers hastened after it.

From the outside, the rabbi's house in Široká Street looked the same as the other simple little houses of the inhabitants of the Jewish Quarter, except perhaps for the stone lion carved above its doors. But when the emperor arrived there the next day and stepped inside, he was inwardly astounded, although he made sure not to show it. He found himself in a spacious palace with wide corridors. Intricate tapestries and golden drapes hung from the walls, the stairs were of marble, and thick carpets on the floor muffled the emperor's steps. The rabbi received the emperor with all honour, and led him into a superb hall where they sat down to a lavish feast. After dinner the rabbi entertained the emperor with his spells, and showed him a quite extraordinary thing – a kind of magic lantern with which he could conjure up images of foreign lands and regions on the wall, and among them an image of Hradčany and Prague Castle.

The visit convinced the emperor that the rabbi of the Jewish community was a man of exceptional wisdom, powers and wealth. He immediately reversed his decree and the Jews were allowed to stay in Prague. From that time on, the learned rabbi was often invited to Prague Castle where he would talk and debate with the learned men of the imperial court. In return, they would often visit the rabbi's study, especially the emperor's court astronomer Tycho de Brahe.

Later there was a rumour that far away from Prague, in some foreign land, at just the time of the emperor's first visit to the rabbi, a whole castle suddenly vanished. Just for a day and a night, for on the morrow it was back in its place. But whoever could believe a thing like that?

The Golem
Old New Synagogue, Červená 2

There were many times when the wise Rabbi Low managed to avert all kinds of perils that threatened the inhabitants of the Jewish Quarter, but he knew too well that he would not live for ever. He therefore took thought as to how he might protect his people and make provision for the future. For a long time he studied in learned books and parchments fragile with age until at last he found what he was seeking. He decided to create an artificial man, endowed with supernatural power, who would help the Jews in hard times and in the fight against their enemies. He confided in his two most talented pupils, and together they went down to the cellar of the rabbi's house and modelled a figure of more than human size out of clay - a golem. When it was ready, the rabbi turned to one of his pupils and said, "Your nature is of fire, so walk round the golem seven times while reciting the sacred words."

The pupil obeyed. When he walked around the first time, the wet clay began to dry out. When he walked round it a second time, the golem began to radiate heat. And by the seventh circumambulation, it was red hot.

"Now it'syour turn, for your nature is of water," said the rabbi to the other pupil.

The pupil walked round the recumbent golem, reciting as he went, and the red-hot matter gradually cooled. By the seventh circumambulation, the golem's body had the colour and temperature of human skin.

Then the rabbi himself walked around the clay creature. Loudly he uttered the sacred words, and after the seventh circle he stopped and placed the holy Shem, a piece of parchment with secret symbols, between the golem's lips. All three waited tensely to see what would happen. The golem's body trembled, his eyes opened, and, after a moment, the golem sat up. His size was terrifying, and when he stood up, his shoulders touched the ceiling vault. He looked very much like a man but could not speak, because the mystery of speech is the most sacred of all, and not even the rabbi knew how to imbue his creation with it. They dressed the golem in the clothes worn by servants in the synagogue, and the rabbi led it up to his wife in the kitchen. "I have taken on a new servant," he told her, "His name is Josef. He will live with us and help in the synagogue and in our household."

And so it was. By day the golem helped in the synagogue or sat on the bench in the rabbi's kitchen, and by night he walked the streets of the Jewish ghetto and made sure that no-one came to any harm. After a time, it was enough for his terrifying form to come into view and people with evil intentions would rapidly take to their heels. He was obedient, and did everything that was necessary, but sometimes he went too far. For example, one day when the rabbi's wife ordered him to bring water to the tub, he brought so much that he drowned the whole street, and when he was sent for apples, he came back with the whole apple stall together with the terrified apple-seller on his huge shoulders, so that the rabbi's wife could choose the fruit for herself.

There was just one thing that the rabbi Low always had to remember. Before the Friday prayers in the synagogue (the start of the Sabbath, the day of rest), the rabbi had to take the sacred Shem from the golem's mouth so that he too could rest. Otherwise the tremendous power of the golem would go out of control.

One day the rabbi's youngest daughter fell ill. She lay on her bed white and almost lifeless, and the anxious rabbi was at his wit's end, unable to find a way to help her. Because it was Friday and the evening was drawing on, he departed for the synagogue with his head full of worrries and completely forgot about the golem. Meanwhile, the golem was sitting on his bench, but when the time for his rest came and went without the rabbi appearing, he got up and began to walk around the kitchen. He paced from wall to wall, faster and faster, and finally ran out into the street. There he ran amok, smashing windows, pulling down wooden house signs and tearing them into pieces with his bare hands, breaking down doors and pulling up trees by their roots. When there was nothing left around for him to break, he went back into the rabbi's house and started to destroy the furniture, smash the crockery, and tear down the pictures and rugs from the wall in his frenzy.

The rabbi was just starting the Sabbath chant when his maid-servant burst into the synagogue and wailingly reported what was happening. The rabbi hesitated, because the psalm that inaugurated the Sabbath had already been sung and nobody was permitted to break the rule of rest after it had sounded. But human lives were at stake, because the golem was capable of killing, as well as destroying, and so the rabbi ran out of the synagogue and hastened home, where the golem was smashing the last piece of furniture with an axe. "Josef, stop!" cried the rabbi in a powerful voice. The golem became gentle as a lamb, obediently sat down in his place in the kitchen where the fragments of the wooden bench now lay, allowed the Shem to be taken from his mouth and became as inanimate as an ordinary mountain of clay.

The rabbi then went back to the synagogue and continued with the prayers. He sang the psalm that proclaims the coming of the Sabbath once again from the beginning, and, from that time onwards, the ninetieth psalm is always sung twice in the Old New

Synagogue to commemorate the event, a ritual carried out in no other synagogue in the world.

Returning home from his evening worship, the rabbi went straight to his sick daughter. As if by a miracle she had recovered, and was simply a little pale from fright.

Rabbi Low knew very well what might have happened if he had not intervened in time. With a heavy heart he made a decision. He summoned the pupils who had helped him to create the golem, and together with the golem, they went up to the attic of the Old New Synagogue. There the rabbi ordered the golem to lie down and shut his eyes. All three of them stood at his head and recited the sacred words backwards. As they recited, the golem's breath gradually weakened until it ceased altogether. Then the rabbi took the Shem from the golem's mouth, walked backwards round the body seven times, and then told his first pupil to do likewise. The golem's skin gradually became grey, until it was the colour of ordinary clay, When the second pupil walked round the golem seven times backwards, its body started to crack and crumble. The three then covered the motionless clay figure with remnants of old cloth and rags.

The next day the rabbi told his wife and the others that the servant Josef had left Prague and would never return. And he forbade anyone to climb to the attic of the Old New Synagogue, for fear that someone might revive the golem.

One unhappy wretch was nevertheless to try.

Centuries later, a poor student heard about the golem. He got it into his head that so strong a servant might help to make his fortune, and he tirelessly studied old Jewish writings until he discovered the sacred texts necessary to bring the clay giant to life. He made a Shem with secret signs and set off for the Jewish Quarter. During the night, he climbed up to the attic of the Old New Synagogue, pulled away the rotten rags, cleaned the golem's body and put the Shem into its mouth. After a moment the cracks in the golem's body started to heal, the golem's body started to glow and clouds of smoke rose out of it. Then the giant trembled, opened his eyes, sat up and finally rose to its feet. Suddenly it started to grow, larger and larger, dreadful and powerful as a red-hot clay mountain. The petrified student quickly tore the Shem from the golem's mouth, and in an instant the golem went rigid. His huge clay body tilted, and fell directly on top of the student, who was buried under a mass of dry clay.

The Children's Plague
The Old Jewish Cemetery, Široká 3

Plague was the most feared disease in the Middle Ages. The infection would spread widely and the sick died in hundreds and thousands because there was no effective treatment for the disease. In the times of Rabbi Löw, a plague broke out in the Jewish Ghetto, but what was strange was that only small children died of it, while adults did not even catch it. Prayers to God to avert the blows of the plague sounded continually in the synagogue, but to no avail, and every day anguished parents laid more children to rest in the Old Jewish Cemetery. Soon people began to murmur that the dead children had found no peace, and that every night they were creeping out of their graves and dancing around the cemetery. Rabbi Low heard the reports and thought of a way of finding out more. He instructed his most courageous pupil to hide in the cemetery and, when the children appeared at midnight, to pull the shroud off one of them and bring it to him quickly.

The pupil obeyed. He hid in the cemetery behind one of the biggest tombstones and waited. Hardly had midnight sounded when small white figures in white shirts climbed out of the graves. They capered and chased each other round the tombstones like living children. The pupil plucked up more courage, and when one of the children dashed around him, he put out a hand, tore off the child's shirt and hastened back to the rabbi's house. Breathless, he flew into the parlour and gave the shroud to the rabbi. The rabbi bowed his head and waited. When the clock struck an hour after midnight, something tapped faintly at the window and a thin little voice called out, "Give me my shroud. I can't go back to my grave without it!"

"I'll give it to you, but only if you tell me why the plague is killing Jewish children," said the rabbi. At first there was only weeping and more piteous pleas from behind the window, but the rabbi was adamant.

"Very well, I'll tell you," the child agreed at last, "It is because a mother killed her child, and until she is punished the plague will continue. And until that time not even those of us who have died shall have rest. Now give me my shroud back!" begged the child. The rabbi opened the window and threw the shroud outside, and the child vanished.

The very next day the rabbi tracked down the cruel mother. The elders of the Jewish Town decided that she must pay for her deed with her life. When the punishment had been carried out, the plague stopped, and from that time on no children haunted the cemetery at night.

Death in a Drop of Dew
The Old Jewish Cemetery, Široká 3

Rabbi Yehuda Löw ben Bezalel lived to a very great age. They say that this was because at the cemetery gate he once met a tall pale woman with a paper in her hand. He knew immediately that it was Death. The rabbi quickly snatched the list with the names of those who were supposed to die that night from her hand, and tore it up; his name had been written there among others. "This time you have escaped, but beware of me!" warned Death. And over the years she lay in wait for him, taking all kinds of forms to deceive him – once as a fisherman who offered him a fish, once as a student who wished to be his pupil, once as a flying dove. But the wise rabbi always recognised Death and evaded her. In the end, however, Death got the better of him. As he was resting in his house, his dearest granddaughter brought him an exquisite fragrant rose. The rabbi forgot his caution, smiled at the little girl, closed his eyes and breathed the fragrance deeply. And as soon as he breathed it in, he fell dead to the ground. Thus he too was conquered by Death, who had hidden herself in the drops of dew on one of the rose's open petals.

Yet it is also said that the rabbi has not yet died completely. For centuries people have been coming to his gravestone in the Old Jewish Cemetery and slipping little pieces of paper with their wishes through the cracks between the stones, hoping that he will grant them. The rabbi sits inside his grave and goes on reading the old books. Only after centuries will one of his descendants come to him and say, "Great Rabbi, the question is resolved!" The rabbi will sigh and crumble into dust.

Poor Pinkas
The Pinkas Synagogue, Široká 3

Centuries ago in the Jewish Town there lived a poor man called Pinkas. He bought and sold old clothes, but it was not enough to support his large family. They would all have died of hunger years before if a rich count, who admired Pinkas for his honesty, had not occasionally given him some money. One thing, however, annoyed the count about Pinkas: the poor man never thanked him for the money, but always just raised his eyes to heaven and cried, "Oh God, I thank you that you have not abandoned me in my need and have helped me!"

When Pinkas came to the count again for money before a feast day, the count deliberately gave him none. He put on a grave face and explained that, "this time want has afflicted me too, Pinkas. But I am sure that your God will help you, when you always thank him so nicely!"

This time Pinkas returned home gloomily, and his family was downcast when he arrived with empty hands. "It will be a sad feast day", said Pinkas to his wife as they lay down to sleep, "but I believe that God will not forget us and will help us survive."

It seemed, however, that this time God was granting him neither money nor rest. In the middle of the night, Pinkas was suddenly awakened by the shattering of glass and then a great thump – a small black shape had flown through the window and fallen to the floor. Pinkas jumped out of bed and pressed himself into a corner, while his wife hid her head under the covers and listened in dread to the malicious laughter coming from the street. Only when the children started to cry with fright did Pinkas recover himself and cautiously inspect the motionless bundle on the floor. It was a dead monkey. Pinkas remembered that he had seen just such a creature on his visits to the count. "This is all we need! Now on top of everything, the count will think I deliberately killed his monkey out of anger!" lamented Pinkas. He had no idea what to do.

It occurred to his wife that they should burn the dead monkey in the stove, so that it would disappear from the world and no-one would find it in their house, but when Pinkas picked it up by the leg to drag it to the kitchen, something tinkled onto the floor. A gold coin! It must have fallen from the monkey's gaping mouth. When they ripped open the monkey, they found a fine heap of ducats in its belly. "You see," Pinkas said to his wife, "God has not abandoned us and has taken care of us!"

They immediately burned the corpse and the next day Pinkas's wife ran to buy food and wine to celebrate the holiday. When the family gathered in the evening around the richly spread table, prayed and prepared to eat, they heard a thumping at the door. It was the count, who had come to see how Pinkas's family was celebrating the holiday without his money. He was amazed when he came into the parlour and saw so much food and drink on the table. Pinkas described what had happened truthfully. He confessed that they had burned the dead monkey and then he brought all the ducats that they had found in the monkey's entrails out of the chamber.

The count was not angry. "I know you didn't kill my monkey, Pinkas, for she disappeared several days ago. And I believe I know how the gold coins got into her stomach. I have a habit of biting gold coins between my teeth to test them. The monkey saw me and must have thought I was swallowing the gold. She copied me, swallowed the money, and when she had filled her belly, she crawled off somewhere and expired. People found her dead body and wanted to give you a fright by throwing it through your window at night."

The count refused to accept the money from Pinkas. "I wanted to punish you and I was curious to see if your God would help you. And he did indeed help you. So the money is yours!"

The money found in the monkey's belly brought Pinkas good fortune. He used it well, expanded his trade and soon became rich. But he always remembered those who hadn't enjoyed the same good luck. In the street where he lived he had a synagogue built, which bears his name.

The Water Goblin's Bride
Zlatá ulice/Gold Street (which no longer exists)

In the Jewish Town there once lived a rabbi who had a beautiful daughter. Hana was quiet by nature, and did not enjoy the noisy company of the other girls. In the evening, she often used to walk to the river and sit in her favourite place between the trees, where the branches leaned down towards the surface of a deep pool. In summer she sometimes took off her dress and bathed there, and then sat on the bank combing her long black hair. She had no idea that she was being watched by a young water goblin who had been entranced by her beauty. One evening he showed himself to her. He looked like a man, strapping and comely, but he had pale skin and green hair. Hana took fright and wanted to flee, but when the water goblin spoke and avowed his love, she came back to the pool to see him. Before long she had fallen in love with him. A few stolen moments soon seemed too little for their love. Not a day went by without the water goblin trying to persuade her to run away from home and live with him in his palace at the bottom of the Vltava. One evening, Hana agreed and never came home again.

Her parents looked for her all night. Men with torches searched the banks, and some trawled the shallows by the banks with long poles to see if they could find her drowned body, but Hana was never seen on dry land again. After a while her parents and relatives reconciled themselves to the thought that Hana had drowned and the currents had borne her body away, so far that they would never find it.

No-one knew that Hana was living happily with the young water goblin in a beautiful house on the river bottom. She lacked for nothing and had enough of everything, and the water goblin's love more than made up for a life without the sun, birds and flowers. After a time, Hana found that she was expecting a child. She asked the water goblin to go and fetch her aunt, who was a midwife. At first, the aunt was reluctant to go with the strange young man with green hair, but when she heard that Hana had sent him, she packed her bag with all she needed and set off with him for the river. The two women were overjoyed to see each other, and everyone was even more delighted when soon the aunt helped to deliver a baby boy with green hair. Then she desired to stay no longer and prepared to leave. Hana offered her some advice, "When the water goblin asks you what you would like in recompense for your help, do not choose pearls or precious stones. Just ask for a little ordinary coal."

The aunt was puzzled but did as Hana told her. At night the water goblin lifted her from the river and she hurried home with an apron full of coal. But because there were holes in her apron she left pieces of coal scattered all over the street. At home she threw the apron and coal into a corner and went off to bed. In the morning she was woken by a great clamour and commotion under her windows. When she looked out she saw people picking up pieces of gold in the street. She rushed to look into the apron – it was full of gold! From that time on the little street in the Jewish Town was known as Zlatá (Gold Street).

Gold in a Dirty Rag
Maisel Synagogue, Maiselova 8 and 10

One day the mayor of the Jewish Quarter, Yitzchak, was returning to Prague from a long journey. His coach drove through a deep forest, dusk fell and it became completely dark among the trees. The horses slowed to a mere walk. The mayor dozed off, waking up every so often just to look out of the window to see if they were already approaching the city. Suddenly he saw a strange golden light among the trees. Being an inquisitive man, he stopped the coach, got out and quietly crept towards the light.

Drawing closer, he saw from behind a great tree trunk that the light was coming from a huge heap of money that was lying there. By the heap stood two dwarves with long beards, taking the gold and silver and filling a sack with it. The mayor was a little afraid, but curiosity got the better of him and he came out of his hiding place, greeted the dwarves politely and asked them who the money belonged to.

"Not to you!" retorted one of the dwarves. The other was more communicative. He grinned at Yitzchak and said,

"When your daughter gets married, you'll find out who it belongs to!"

This did not satisfy the mayor. He considered for a moment, thought up a plan for discovering the owner of the treasure, and asked the dwarves if he might exchange three coins from the heap for his own. The dwarves did not object. Yitzchak took three gold coins from the heap and replaced them with three gold pieces from the pouch that he wore on his belt. Hardly had he done so when the light went out and the dwarves disappeared into the darkness with the treasure. The mayor went back to his coach, but told no-one what he had seen. After a while, they rode out of the forest and the city was already in sight.

The next morning curiosity tormented Yitzchak just as it had the previous evening. He took one of the coins from the treasure, wrapped it up in a dirty rag, placed the rag in the road in front of his house and watched all day to see who would pick up the knotted cloth. Towards evening a grubby looking little lad ran up, nimbly snatched the rag with the gold piece and vanished before the mayor could collect himself. The following day the mayor repeated the trap, and when the lad came up again towards evening and took the gold piece, it was clear that this was no accident. On the third day he lay in wait for the lad. The boy was just picking up the knotted rag when the mayor grabbed him by the arm.

"Pardon me Sir, I didn't know I was doing anything wrong," protested the boy, on the edge of tears, and stretched out his hand to return the gold piece. The mayor calmed the boy, took him into the house, gave him food and inquired where he was from and where he lived. Then he asked how the boy knew he was supposed to pick up a rag thrown down in the street on three successive days.

"For three nights I had the same dream," said the boy, "telling me to run to your house and pick up the gold piece in a rag that would be lying in front of it."

The mayor no longer doubted that the boy was the person to whom the treasure would one day belong. He decided that he liked young Mordechai Maisel, as the boy was called. After a time the mayor went to see the lad's parents, who had a small ironmonger's business on the very edge of the Jewish Quarter. He offered to give the boy an education and an appropriate upbringing. The parents were happy to agree, since they could not have afforded such benefits themselves. And so from that time on little Mordechai grew up in the family of the Mayor Yitzchak. He was clever, hardworking and quick to learn, and he was far from ugly. So it was no wonder that a few years later the Mayor's daughter fell in love with him. The

119

mayor had secretly reckoned with the match and readily arranged the young couple's wedding.

Yet the thought of the pile of money continued to gnaw at him. His daughter had already married, but where was the gold? The weeks and months went by and nothing happened. Yitzchak even took his son-in-law to the place where years before he had encountered the dwarves with the treasure. He didn't tell Mordechai why they were going to the forest. He simply had the idea that if the money was not coming to Mordechai, perhaps he should go to the money. Together they criss-crossed the forest, tramping about in it all day long, but they encountered nothing at all odd.

Deep down, Yitzchak began to be annoyed that he had allowed himself to be deceived and had married his daughter to a poor man. And he failed to keep his anger to himself, conceiving such an aversion for his son-in-law that Mordechai and his wife eventually moved out of his house. Mordechai took over his parents' shop and soon became one of the best merchants in the town. He became rich but not proud, giving money to the poor and always keeping his doors open to the needy.

It happened one summer that a peasant came to Mordechai to choose an iron tool. Saying that he had insufficient money to pay, he gave Mordechai a heavy iron crate as security, and promised to come for it in the autumn with enough money to pay his debt. But the months went by and nobody came for the crate. When a year had passed and then another, Mordechai opened the crate – it was full of gold and silver coins!

Thus in the end the treasure reached Mordechai Maisel. When Mordechai told his father-in-law how he had acquired it, the mayor finally told him his own story. Mordechai didn't want to believe it, for what if the peasant came back after all? Yitzchak smiled, "Don't wait for the peasant! He was certainly one of the dwarves!"

Mordechai Maisel spent the money wisely and not just on himself. He used it to build a new synagogue, which was later named after him, and then a Jewish town hall, baths, almshouse and refuge for orphans. And the winding Jewish alleys were paved at his expense. He remained a rich man to his death, and now rests in the Old Cemetery.

The New Town

THE NEW TOWN

Vltava

Staré
Město

Václ. nám.

Karlovo
nám.

67

68

60

59

64

62

66

61

63

65

69

The Founding of the New Town

One day the Emperor and King Charles IV held a feast at Prague Castle for his friends and the leading nobles in the land. When they had dined, they went to take the air on the stone inner gallery of the palace. It was a warm summer's night, the stars were shining in the sky and Prague spread out beneath them. The moonlight fell on the gables and roofs of the houses, churches and towers, and the water murmured as it flowed over the weirs of the Vltava. The king turned to his astronomer and commanded, "Tell us what the heavenly signs say at this moment about the future of our city!"

The astronomer was at first reluctant to reply but then confessed what he could read in the stars. The Smaller Town, (today Malá Strana - the Lesser Town) would be destroyed by fire, and the Old Town washed away by a great flood. Not a stone of Prague would be left standing. Everyone was stunned by this ominous news. Even the king fell silent, but then he turned to the city, raised his hand and cried, "My city will not vanish from the world so easily! And if the Lesser Town and the Old Town meet with destruction, there will remain another town I shall have built!"

The king did as he had proclaimed. He ordered plans to be drawn up for a grand, immense town, which would stretch from the Old Town walls as far as Vyšehrad. The town he founded and built was given the name of Prague New Town.

Nekázanka

Nekázanka

A narrow street called Nekázanka leads from Na Příkopě to Jindřišská Street. It is said to have acquired the name at the time when the New Town was just being created. Having decided to establish the New Town, Charles IV personally supervised the drawing and measuring of the streets and land parcels, so that everything should be exactly as he wished. But he was compelled to leave Prague for a while. On his return he went to the building site to check how the work was progressing, and noticed a street that had not been on the plans he had approved. "Where did that street come from?" he demanded angrily.

The builders were alarmed, fearing that that the king would punish them for their mistake, and they couldn't get a single word out. When the king saw their confusion, he laughed and said, "Very well. Let the street stay. But let it forever be called Nekázalka, to remind people that I didn't order it to be built!" The Czech word means something like "not ordered". As time went by people started to call it Nekázanka, not Nekázalka, and they still do today. Nekázanka means something "disordered" and historians claim that the name is actually derived from the disorderly, uninhibited life led by its inhabitants.

Faust's House
Karlovo náměstí 40 - 41

In the corner of Karlovo náměstí (Charles Square), opposite the Na Slovanech Monastery, stands an ancient house, or to be more precise a small palace. Legend tells that it once belonged to Doctor Faustus, who sold his soul to the devil. One night the devil came for him and he vanished, leaving nothing but a scorched gaping hole in one of the rooms. Nobody could succeed in bricking up the hole, for the masonry always fell out again overnight, and so the house remained empty and people were terrified of spending even one night there.

Until a student, Mladota by name, was audacious enough to enter Faust's House. One night, he had been forced to pack up his meagre possessions and leave his poor lodgings with a bundle on his back because he already owed weeks of rent. With nowhere to lay his head he tramped through the streets of Prague until he found himself in front of Faust's House. And because he was a stranger to fear he said to himself, "Why should I spend the night under a bridge when there's a whole palace waiting for me here?" He tentatively pressed down the rusty handle, and the front door scraped open. In the moonlight, everything had a spectral look: he could make out twisted furniture and strange statues in shadowy corners, a spacious kitchen with a big table and chairs, a study with scrolls of parchment and books, all covered with a layer of dust and yellowed. In a bedroom the student found a fine bed with a canopy, and so he wasted no time but flung aside the dusty counterpane, lay down under the quilt and fell sound asleep. When he woke in the morning he looked around curiously. He was most interested by the study, which was partially equipped as a laboratory. Apart from books and scrolls, the long table held a quantity of bottles, alembics and retorts, still with remnants of the original contents. And in the midst of this disorder, lying in a stone bowl - a polished silver thaler coin! What luck, thought the student. He took the thaler, didn't stay long in the house but hurried off to find his friends in the tavern. He told them about the comfortable lodgings he had found for himself and he had enough money for a good meal and several beers. In fact, he drank to his good fortune with his friends so thoroughly that twilight caught him in the same tavern, and so he went off to sleep at Faust's house again. He sank into the quilts, fell asleep, and when he woke, the sun was already high in the sky. Something seemed to whisper in his ear, telling him to go and see if there might not be another coin in the bowl. And there it was - round, shining and silver. "I could get to like the sort of ghost who brings you money!" thought the student. He went straight to the tavern and everything happened just as on the day before. Soon he became accustomed to this strange way of life. Every morning he would take the thaler from the bowl, drink it away with his friends, and then go back at night to sleep, and he forgot his studies entirely. His friends envied him his luck, but, in the depths of their hearts, none would have exchanged their lives for his. Mladota was too reckless and it never occurred to him that there had to be a price for this kind of magical favour.

One day, he didn't go to the tavern. It struck him that instead of just one thaler he might be able to find several in the bowl, or why not gold pieces! He dusted off the books of sorcery and started to read them. The largest in particular engrossed him. He leafed through it until late into the night, and then again the next day. Since he had after all learned something from his studies he soon deciphered their strange script and realised that they were spells to conjure up dark spirits.

A week went by and the student had not appeared among his friends. It occurred to them that he might be ill, and so a few brave souls among them set out for the Faust House to pay him a visit. But they knocked vainly at the front door until one of them had the idea of climbing over the wall into the garden and then getting into the palace through a window. Once inside, they looked for Mladota and called his name, but there was no answer. When they entered the study a terrible sight met their eyes. Everything had been destroyed, the books torn up and the vessels shattered, the table with the great book overturned...And in the ceiling there was a great black hole. Full of horror, the students fled from the Faust House, and then told everyone that the devil himself had carried Mladota away through the hole in the ceiling.

Lokýtek
The New Town Hall, Karlovo náměstí 23

Fixed into the masonry of the tower of the New Town Hall is an iron '*loket*' (in English an 'ell'- from 'elbow' - which is also the literal meaning of the Czech word), an official measure of length, which in the past everyone could use to check that merchants had not been cheating when selling them cloth. Because the *loket* was set a little high, some people couldn't reach up to it and so the councillors hired a tall man to stand by the *loket* and measure the fabric for the people. Because he stood by the *loket*, people began to call him Loket. When he died, his son inherited his measuring job. The son was not so tall, however, and had to use a ladder to measure the cloth, and so people nicknamed him 'Little Loket', or in Czech 'Lokýtek'.

Lokýtek was not only shorter but less honest than his father. He had pleasant and easy work, but that was not enough for him and he wanted more money. So he made a secret agreement with some of the drapers. When he measured cloth sold by the drapers who paid him, he always said that the measurements were correct even when they had sold their customers short, and when the cloth was from drapers who had not paid him, he always gave an unfavourable measurement regardless of the truth. As soon as someone asked him to check a measurement, Lokýtek would go up his ladder and would casually say, "Nice cloth, who did you buy it from?", and the result would depend on the answer. The honest drapers had no inkling how Lokýtek was treating their goods. People stopped buying from them and some of them ended up in penury as a result of the measurer's dishonesty.

One honest draper, however, refused to give up. He worked out why it was that people were no longer coming to his shop, and decided to test Lokýtek. He himself measured out a correct length of cloth and took the roll to the New Town Hall. Because it was market day and a whole crowd of people were pressing around the *loket*, Lokýtek asked his usual question without looking properly, "Who did you buy it from?" The draper gave his own name. Lokýtek measured the cloth and then sadly shook his head, "Oh dear, I'm afraid he's sold you seriously short, don't you go buying there again!"

"What?" shouted the draper, "Now I'm going to measure it myself, you cheat!" He pushed Lokýtek aside, measured the cloth and showed that it was correct to the last fraction of an inch.

"Just take a look at this cunning scoundrel!" cried the draper, "He makes fools of you all, blackening the honest and giving preferential treatment to the dishonest!" For a moment, the people stood bewildered, but then they understood what had happened. Many of them added their protests to the draper's and started to advance on the measurer shouting. Lokýtek wasted no time in turning round

129

and hurrying away. And they say that nobody ever saw him again. The poor draper was so enraged that he fell ill and died the next day. The story goes that on each anniversary of the draper's death Lokýtek's ghost appears by the *loket*, runs around the New Town Hall with fevered staring eyes like a hunted man, and then vanishes for another year.

The Cook from the Emmaeus Monastery
The Church and Monastery Na Slovanech, Vyšehradská 49

The Church and Monastery Na Slovanech have also been known as Emmaeus since time immemorial, because the altar painting in the church showed Jesus with his disciples in Emmaeus. A legend tells that the monks in the Emmaeus Monastery were so pious that the devil decided he must get their souls whatever it cost him. Fortune was in his favour, for the monastery cook had just died, and so the devil took on the form of a cook and the monks accepted him in their monastery kitchen. Instead of plain monastery fare, the devil started to cook delicacies like quail breast, smoked ham, the best sausages, game and pâté, and served them with excellent choice wines. Gradually the monks forgot thoughts of prayer and talked only of food and drink, lived it up and made merry, and became fat and lazy. The devil was exceedingly pleased.

One day the abbot was passing the kitchen on his way to bed and heard strange voices. Curious, he stopped at the door to listen, wondering who the cook was talking to. Inside, the diabolical cook was just telling another devil, who was visiting him from hell, how well his plans were going and how he would soon be carrying the souls of the pleasure-loving monks off to hell. As soon as the abbot heard this, he burst into the kitchen and confounded the devilish chef, who immediately turned into a cock and flew away through the window. From that time on the monks of Emmaeus were doubly pious to make sure that none would drop their guard against the snares of hell.

The Silver Fish
Myslíkova 14

On the corner of what is today Myslíkova Street and Spálená Street stands a house that bears the name 'At the Myslíks', after the family who once owned it. In the period after the Battle of the White Mountain in 1620, hundreds of Protestant nobles and burghers had to leave the country to avoid persecution by the Catholics. The owner of the House U Myslíků and his family were among those compelled to flee. There was no question of their being able to take more with them than could be carried on their backs in knapsacks.

The evening before their departure, the father of the family had all the silver in the house gathered together, plates, goblets, pots and spoons. The sons beat them flat and the father melted them down in a cauldron over the fire. Then they took a large clay baking form in the shape of a fish and poured the molten silver into it. When the silver had cooled down, they turned it out of the form, pulled out one of the wooden panels that lined the largest room, and hid the silver fish in a small niche in the wall. Then they slid the panel back so that no-one would suspect a thing. They believed that one day they or their descendants would come back and retrieve the silver, but neither the father nor his sons nor any member of the family ever returned to the house.

The house then passed through the hands of many different owners, and none of them made any great repairs. When the house was already in danger of falling down, the Prague City Council decided that it must be demolished so as not to be a danger to the surrounding area, and a new one must be built. For the owner this was an absolute calamity, for he was by no means rich and had to borrow a lot of money for construction of the new house. He began demolition with a heavy heart, but when the workmen were tearing down the wall in the largest room, they found a great heavy fish of black metal in the masonry of the wall, and how great was the astonishment of the owner when he discovered that the fish was made of pure silver, which had merely gone black with age! The sale of the fish brought the owner so much money that he could pay off his debts with plenty to spare for building the new house.

The Water Goblin's Children
The vanished village of Podskalí

Podskalí, or 'Under the Rock' was originally a fishing and lumbering village that lay between Vyšehrad and what today is Resslova Street. For almost a thousand years the village was the home of sand collectors, fishermen, ferrymen, raftsmen and the icemen who supplied the town cellars with ice for keeping the food stocks cool. At the beginning of the twentieth century the old village houses of Podskalí were torn down to make way for new apartment houses and whole streets.

Like the trades of its inhabitants, everyday life in Podskalí was closely bound up with the Vltava River. This meant that all the Podskalí children learned to swim before they could walk. Nonetheless, it was not infrequent for children to drown. Once the victim was the son of a poor fisherman who had a small cottage on the edge of the bank. His wife was inconsolable, for all the rest of her children were daughters, and the boy had been her only son, and she wept and wailed even more when the children told her what exactly had happened. The boy had been jumping and fooling about with the other children on the rafts tied up at the bank when suddenly a water goblin had emerged and dragged the boy down under the water. Hearing this, the unfortunate mother in all her despair cursed the water goblin's children. "May they never be able to get back into the water if ever they leave it!" she cried.

Her curse was fulfilled that very night. When the moon swung up from behind the horizon, the water goblin's children climbed up out of the water onto the rafts and began to chase each other and play just like human children. Towards morning they wanted to jump back into the Vltava, but they could not: they remained on the rafts as if someone had glued them there. They called and wept until the old water goblin came up to help them, but his efforts were in vain, and the children had to stay in the rafts. The night departed, morning came and the sun started to shine. Its light and heat burned the unhappy little goblins like fire and dried out their green skin. Water goblins can only survive on dry land so long as the mist keeps them wet, and if they dry out entirely, they perish. So that day in Podskalí was full of wailing and grief: the little water goblins on the raft wept, the old water goblin sobbed heart-rendingly under the bank, and the fisherman's grieving wife lamented in the little cottage.

Towards evening the wise woman of Podskalí knocked on the cottage door. She knew how to treat sick bodies and minds and was well aware that the curse of the fisherman's wife would lead to no good. For hours she tried to persuade the wife to take the boy's shirt, wet with her tears, and throw it to the little water goblins, for then the curse would be lifted and the water goblin's children would be able to go back to the Vltava. No-one could ever give her son his life back, and who would it help if other innocent children died as well? Night had already fallen by the time the wife agreed. Tears were streaming down her face as she took her son's shirt and took it down to the riverside. Scarcely had she reached the bank when the old water goblin raised his hand from the water and promised that he would never again drown any child of Podskalí. The fisherman's wife threw the shirt to the children, and fled back into the cottage with never a look behind her.

As soon as the shirt touched the little goblins it was as if new blood flowed into their veins. They could raise their short little legs from the boards of the raft and one after another they slipped into the water, into their father's embrace. And just as the water goblin promised, since then no child has drowned in Podskalí.

The Mermaid of the Pool
V Tůních

Before the New Town was built, where Žitná Street and Ječná Street lie today, there were only small village houses, and around them meadows, fields and gardens. Where you find the street called V Tůních (At the Pools), there were really pools, and the street Na rybníčku (At the Little Fishpond) gets its name from what was a real fishpond and a hamlet of the same name.

The legend runs that a beautiful mermaid used to sit by the pools. On summer nights her sad singing carried as far as the hamlet, and her beauty was such that many local lads became infatuated with her. If any came close to her, however, she would just jump into the pool and disappear. Until the time when a boy fell deeply and passionately in love with her. He thought about her wherever he went, spent his evenings by the pool and would watch the mermaid from a safe hiding place as she sang her sad songs and adorned her hair with the coltsfoot flowers that grew here. Once, in despair at his unrequited love, when the mermaid slid back into the pool the young man kissed the leaves of the flowers she had touched a moment before. The next evening when the mermaid climbed onto the bank again, she touched the same blossoms and laid them to her cheek. The young man could no longer contain himself, but leapt out and caught her in his embrace. The mermaid wanted to tear herself from

135

his arms, but could not, for her face had been touched by the lad's kiss left on the coltsfoot blossom, and so she had to stay.

The lad begged the mermaid not to forsake him, and said he would take her home and marry her. The mermaid burst into tears and told him her story. She was the daughter of a raftsman who had drowned in the Vltava in an unfortunate accident. Her mother had then brought home a new groom, but he had fallen in love with her daughter. Angry, her mother had cursed her, "May the water always be her home, as it is to her poor father!" When the groom found out what the mother had done to her own daughter, he killed her and then drowned himself. And so the mermaid had to live in the pool and could only be set free by a young man whose mother would give her her son and accept her as a daughter.

"Stop weeping," the youth comforted the mermaid, "for my mother loves me and will not spoil my happiness. She will certainly give us her blessing and arrange our wedding!" The mermaid listened to his words with hope, calmed herself and accepted the lad's promise that the next day he would come to the pool with his mother. Full of joy, the lad ran home and told his mother everything. She agreed to go to the pool with him the next day.

When the mermaid came out of the water that evening she saw the youth and his mother on the bank, but as soon as the mother spied the mermaid, she immediately began to scold and shout, "You unnatural creature, how dare you take a fancy to my son? Go back into the water and marry a water goblin or some other monster like yourself!"

The mermaid slipped back into the pool like a fish, and from the depths her loud laments and sobs could be heard rising to the surface. The young man stood for a moment as if turned to stone, but then he jumped in after his beloved and the water closed over his head forever. For the rest of her life his mother would mourn her son and regret her hastiness. The mermaid was never seen again, but many people heard her despairing weeping in the night. It is said that the mermaid is still weeping there in the underground sources to this day, but in the noise of the great metropolis no-one one can hear her any longer.

The Executioner's Sword
Štvanice island

In olden times the profession of executioner was considered unclean, and so executioners were not allowed to live among other people but only in solitary places far beyond the city walls. People recoiled from them by day but secretly visited them at night when they needed help, for thanks to their dreadful profession executioners had a good knowledge of the human body and knew how to treat wounds and cure sicknesses. The same was true of the New Town executioner, who lived in a small house on the island of Štvanice.

One evening a mother with a small son knocked at his door. The boy was constantly sick, no medicine did him any good and the doctors only shrugged their shoulders helplessly. When the mother stepped with her boy through the executioner' door, she was immediately afraid, for it seemed to her that there had been a flash of light on the opposite wall where the executioner's great sword hung. She also noticed that the executioner's face went pale and he was altogether disconcerted, and so with dread she asked him what the sign meant. The executioner was reluctant to tell her but in the end gave

in. "That is how my sword speaks. It moves when someone enters whose blood it is fated to shed, and your boy is such a one."

The mother burst into loud weeping and would not be calmed. Was the life of her little son destined to end with the executioner's sword? She threw herself on her knees before the executioner and begged him to help avert this dreadful doom. The executioner was a good-hearted man, and knew what to do, as well. "If you allow it, I shall take my sword and make the tiniest cut on one of the boy's fingers. Then the prophecy will have been fulfilled."

The mother consented through her tears. The executioner took the sword down and ran its sharp edge along the boy's forefinger, just enough for one drop of blood to appear. Then he examined the boy and gave the mother a bunch of herbs to make an infusion for her son to bring back his health. And so it happened. The boy recovered, and when he grew up he became a respected citizen who lived out his life in peace and content.

The Treasure of Na Poříčí
The Church of St. Peter Na Poříčí, Petrské Square.

When Charles IV decided to build the New Town he included within the New Town Walls several settlements that were already standing on the territory. One such settlement was Poříč, which had been established in the eleventh century by German merchants. The Germans had built the Romanesque Church of St. Peter here, which was later reconstructed in Gothic style. St. Peter's Church was surrounded by a graveyard like all the parish churches throughout Prague. Now it happened that a rich burgher died in Poříč. He had been an eccentric, lived alone and been stingy with his money, not even keeping company with his relatives for fear of having to share some of it. Before his death he had already purchased a cheap wooden coffin and slept in it instead of a bed. In fact, they found him dead in the coffin, and buried him in it forthwith. His relatives were looking forward to enjoying the miser's wealth after his death, but search as they might in his house, they just couldn't find the money. They pulled up the floorboards, dug in the cellar, hunted in the attic and tapped at the walls, but they didn't find even a penny.

A few months passed. Then, as the old verger was coming home one night around the graveyard, he suddenly noticed a yellow

light, a jack-o'lantern, dancing in the darkness. It flickered over one grave, and that was the grave of the rich miser. The verger immediately guessed what it meant, for such lights always hovered over places where treasure was buried in the ground. He told his son and they resolved to dig the treasure up. They went into the graveyard at night, first throwing a rosary around the flame to make it stand still and prevent the treasure from sinking right down to the depths of the earth. Then they began to dig. When they broke the coffin lid, under the corpse's head they saw a decayed pillow with golden jewels and money pouring out of it. The stingy burgher had loved his gold too much to wish to leave it to anyone, and so had sewn it into the pillow to be certain that it would be buried with him.

With this treasure the verger and his son became very rich, but they were not miserly like the burgher. They shared the money with the poor and there was enough for everyone to be happy.

The Builder of the Church on Karlov
The Church of the Assumption and St Charles the Great on Karlov, Ke Karlovu Street

The Church of the Assumption and St. Charles the Great was founded on the highest ground in the New Town by the Emperor and King Charles IV in 1350. Its huge vault has an average diameter of 24 metres; it is in the shape of a regular octagon and only 20 centimetres thick in some places. Its builder is said to have been very talented in his craft, but still young and lacking any chance to show what he could do. To make matters worse he was also unhappy in love. The girl loved him in return but her father, a rich New Town burgher, had no desire to give his daughter to a poor suitor. When the young man asked for the hand of his daughter, he told him, "I would be happy to oblige you, but you must realise that I cannot marry my only daughter to a man without a reputation or money. When you come into money and your name means something, come back and we shall see!"

The young man was downcast but did not lose hope. At that time there were reports that the king intended to build a church and monastery on the steep hill above the Brusnice Brook right next to the New Town walls, and a builder had not yet been chosen. This was the opportunity he had been waiting for! He immediately set to work, spending whole days and nights sitting over plans, thinking, calculating, drafting and sketching. He wanted to create a design for a building so extraordinary that the emperor would be quite unable to refuse it. When Charles IV saw the plans he was indeed impressed by the beauty of the design and its audacity, and entrusted the young man with the work. The workmen started to dig the foundations immediately, brought timber and stone on wagons, and soon the walls of the church began to rise skywards. The young builder supervised everything, making decisions, issuing orders, and secretly stroking the slabs of stone with joy that the building was progressing so fast and so well.

But there were envious men who wished him no success. They were chiefly the builders whom the emperor had refused, and they couldn't abide the sound of the young man's name. One of them managed to sneak a look at the plans, and when he saw the huge and audacious vault, he told everyone that the design was impossible, and such a vault would never hold up. Others joined their voices to his, saying that the young builder was inexperienced and unlearned in his craft, that the whole enterprise would end in great shame, and when the scaffolding and the great treetrunk props were removed the audaciously arching vault would collapse and fall. The emperor himself heard this gossip and summoned the youth to tell him what was being said about him. "But I trust you," said the emperor, "and I only hope that you will not disappoint my trust!" The young man went away uneasy. He started to have doubts about his work and to fear that he might indeed disappoint the emperor. What if he had made mistakes in his calculations? He went through his notes and plans, line by line and number by number, but he found no error. Yet instead of disappearing, his doubts continued to grow.

When the workmen had gone home the next day, the young man stayed behind under the high vault supported by the thick trunks. It was already growing dark outside and the light of the torch in his hand lit up the arch, flickered on the walls and cast deep soft shadows in the corners. The builder scrutinised the arch, taking a few steps here and there to consider it from all angles, and his brow was furrowed with care. What if the vault collapsed? His dream of a happy life with his beloved would collapse with it, shattering into pieces like the great slabs of stone. And after such a disgrace could a builder ever win recognition and fame again? All at once he glimpsed a movement in a dark corner. He took fright, wondering what anyone could be doing here at night in the deserted building, and he raised his torch to see the newcomer. The man who emerged from the shadows had a strange dark face and piercing eyes. He spoke in kind tones to the builder, "Do not be afraid, for I have no ill intentions. On the contrary, I wish to help you, because I know what is tormenting you."

The stranger in the expensive black cloak walked up to the builder and said, "I can promise you that the vault will hold up and you will marry the woman you love. And all this in return for just a single signature." From the folds of his cloak the man pulled out a parchment and he handed the young man a sharp quill pen.

The builder immediately knew who the stranger was. He felt he was in a dream. On the one hand he saw fame and riches, and on the other hand the shame, despair and penury to which the building would condemn him if it fell. As if stupefied, he reached for the parchment. The stranger took him by the left hand, and scratched his palm with the sharp quill. He wetted the tip of the quill in the drops of blood that appeared, and gave the quill to the builder. As soon as the latter had signed, the man vanished into the shadows in the corner from which he had come. The young man wanted to believe that it had all been no more than a dream, but the small wound in his palm reminded him that it was not..

Yet at least his despair was gone. That night the young man slept soundly until the morning and woke in a good mood. When he arrived at the building, the workmen hardly recognised him. He smiled and joked, and the work went smoothly. It only remained to remove the scaffolding and the props, but the workmen didn't like the idea, for they feared the vault would fall down on them. They tried to dissuade the builder, threatened and then insisted on their rights. The builder wondered how he could do it by himself, and suddenly someone seemed to whisper in his ear, "Set fire to the scaffolding! The wood will burn up but the stone will not be harmed! Burn it!" Yes, that was the way it had to be done! He ordered bundles of chips and thin branches to be set under the scaffolding, lit a torch and then the fires. The flames shot up high as if helped by a wind, and everything was enveloped in clouds of black smoke that rolled out of the windows and doors in thick spirals. Then in one moment all the props gave way and everything seemed to be collapsing onto the ground with a terrible crash. The builder stood as if struck by lightning. "The devil too has cheated and lied to me!" he thought. There was a roaring in his head, and all around was black smoke. Like a madman he ran around the walls towards the Vltava, reached the river bank and without hesitating for an instant jumped into the water, never to be seen alive again.

It took a long time for the fire to go out, the dust to settle and the smoke to disperse, but when the workmen cautiously went back inside the church they were astounded. The vault was unharmed. Only now could the eye see how lightly it rose above the pillars, beautiful and extraordinary. When the emperor heard the news, he came himself to look at the vault and wished to praise the builder in person, but it was as if the earth had swallowed the young man up and he was nowhere to be found. It was three days later that the fishermen pulled his body from the water. The unfortunate builder had not lived to enjoy praise, glory or his beloved, yet to this day the church on Karlov proclaims the greatness of his art.

Vyšehrad

VYŠEHRAD

Libuše and Přemysl

The legend tells that the first Slavs to arrive in the land were led here by the warrior leader Čech (Czech), who later gave his name to the country. His successor, Krok, died leaving three daughters, Kazi, Teta and Libuše. Kazi was greatly versed in the healing powers of herbs, and knew how to cure people of all kinds of sickness and wounds. Teta was an expert in ancient rites and taught people how to honour the gods and demons of nature. The youngest daughter Libuše was the wisest, and also had the gift of prophecy and could foretell the future. It was therefore Libuše to whom the elders entrusted the government of the land after her father's death. Libuše accepted the responsibility and made her seat in a castle on a high cliff over the Vltava, called Vyšehrad.

One day, two noblemen from the neighbouring villages came to Vyšehrad. They were in dispute over a piece of pasture and wanted Libuše to settle the matter. The princess listened to them, consulted with her counsellors, and then gave judgement. The one in whose favour she ruled thanked the princess for her justice, but his opponent went red with anger and shouted, "How can a woman understand men's affairs? It's not for nothing that people say long hair means little sense. It shames all men that we are ruled by a woman!"

Everyone present froze. The princess was silent for a while, and then spoke, "Very well. Tomorrow I shall tell you the name of the man who will become my husband and Prince of all Bohemia."

The news that the Czechs would have a prince spread like wildfire thought the land. The next day, many people gathered at Vyšehrad, agog with excitement to hear what the princess would say. Libuše sat on her throne and said,

"In the region of the Lemuzi beyond the River Bílina there is a village that belongs to the Stadic clan. There on a field your new Prince Přemysl will be ploughing with two oxen. Tell messengers to take a princely robe and go to him. They must tell him I ask him to take me for his wife and govern in Vyšehrad. My horse will lead you there."

As the princess had spoken, so it happened. Libuše's white horse was led out of the stable and set free, and the messengers followed it. They journeyed untiringly, over mountains and across rivers, until they found themselves in the region of the Lemuzi and reached the village of Stadice. When they spied the field on which a young and strong man was ploughing with two oxen, Libuše's horse stopped and whinnied. The messengers bowed to Přemysl and conveyed Libuše's message to him. Přemysl heard them out as if he had been expecting them, for he showed no astonishment and asked no questions. He unyoked the oxen from the plough, slapped a strong palm across their rumps, and cried, "Go back to the place from which you came!"

The oxen ran to a rock which opened before them, swallowed them up and closed again.

Then Přemysl took the hazel rod he had been using to drive the oxen and stuck it into the ground. As if bewitched, the wand became green, grew up high and sprouted three slender branches with leaves and nuts. Two of the branches withered and dried up, but one rose upwards and bore new fruit. The messengers plucked up courage to ask what this miracle might signify. "My line will be like this hazelnut tree", said Přemysl. "Many men will be born from it, but only one shall rule."

Then Přemysl put on the princely robes and cloak and thrust his old bast shoes into a knapsack that he slung across his shoulders.

The messengers asked what use the prince would have for an ordinary knapsack and old shoes? "These are for my descendants, to remind them of their origins and make sure they do not forget, and do not in their pride oppress those who go through the world with only a knapsack and in bast shoes," Přemysl said with a smile.

The journey back passed quickly. When they rode into the territory of the Czechs, the people in the villages through which they passed joyfully greeted their prince and followed him on foot or on horseback. When the guards at Vyšehrad spied the great procession approaching, they told the princess, and she went straight out to meet Přemysl with her retinue. The wedding ceremonies lasted three days and nights. Libuše placed her hand in Přemysl's palm and together they made sacrifice to the gods, becoming man and wife, prince and princess.

The Founding of Prague

One summer afternoon Libuše, Přemysl and their retinue were looking out from the walls of Vyšehrad. The sun was sinking towards the west and bathing the countryside in golden light. Libuše suddenly went up to the very edge of the walls, stretched out her hand toward the forested hills on the opposite side of the Vltava and started to prophecy. "I see a great and beautiful city, whose fame shall one day touch the stars. There in the woods is a place where you will find a man carving a door threshold for his house (in Czech "práh" means "threshold"). Let a fine castle be built there and call it Praha. And just as every prince and king bows their head before the threshold of a house, so one day even the most powerful shall bow to the castle and the city that will grow up beneath it."

The next day, Přemysl sent out messengers to the place Libuše had spoken of. They found the man carving the threshold of a house, and there they built a castle. As the years went by and the centuries flowed away like the waters of the Vltava into the sea of time, the castle Praha became the seat of the Czech princes and later the Czech kings. And to this day people from all over the world bow before the beauty of the city that bears its name.

The Golden Cradle

It is said that when Libuše gave birth to her first son, she rocked him in a golden cradle. When he grew up she threw the cradle into a deep pool under the rock of Vyšehrad, where it sank to the very bottom. Then she uttered words of prophecy: "The gold of the cradle shall lie at the bottom of the Vltava until a ruler is born in Bohemia who shall be worthy of it!"

The centuries went by and the cradle was never found, until one night it floated up of its own accord when the last woman of the Přemyslid line, Queen Eliška, gave birth to Wenceslas, later the King of Bohemia and Holy Roman Emperor Charles IV. The queen also laid him in the golden cradle, and as he grew the miraculous cradle grew with him. In time it changed into a comfortable couch, in which Charles IV slept as monarch. After his death they say that the magic golden cradle returned to the bottom of the Vltava pool.

The Treasure in the Vyšehrad Rock

Libuše often prophesied by gazing into the flowing waters of the Vltava. One day she had an evil vision, for she beheld a time coming when the land would be gripped by want, hunger and despair. To protect against this threat, she decided to find a great quantity of gold and hide it against hard times. She had her servants seek out places rich in gold ore and mine there. She was helped by a golden frog, for wherever it jumped there was gold. The princess hid the gold ore in a secret hiding place in the Rock of Vyšehrad. When Libuše married Přemysl she showed him the secret treasure, but betrayed its whereabouts to nobody else. Thus it happened that after her death no-one one knew where the treasure lay, and no-one has found it to this day.

The chance of finding the treasure of the Vyšehrad Rock comes just once a year, on Good Friday when the rocks that conceal treasures open up for a short time. But a mortal who searches for it must never look round, whatever happens behind him. The story goes that a villager once made the attempt. One Good Friday he spied an open entrance in the rock and without a moment's hesitation went into a dark passage. He ventured on, and although terrifying voices and screams rang out behind him, he did not turn his head. But when he came to a hall in which glittering piles of gold were all about him, he heard his brother calling and turned round. In that instant there was a great crash and the world went black. When he came to himself he was lying on the grass in front of the Vyšehrad Rock and there was not a trace of the opening.

Bivoj

Once Libuše in Vyšehrad received a visit from her sister Kazi. The sisters were deep in conversation when a commotion and shouting in the courtyard interrupted them. They looked down from the window and saw a young man coming with a huge live boar on his back, accompanied by a clamorous crowd of villagers. Libuše and her sister went out into the courtyard. "Why are you disturbing the peace of my castle?" asked Libuše severely. An old man with white hair and a beard emerged from the crowd, bowed and said,

"Forgive us, Princess, for disturbing you. But for weeks this black boar has devastated the crops in our fields, prowled about in the woods and torn more than one neighbour to bloody shreds. No-one one could be found to stand up to him until Bivoj," the old man pointed a gaunt finger, "Bivoj would have it no other way, but he must place his prey at your feet."

"So be it," said Libuše, "You may put down your burden, Bivoj. The guards will kill it on the spot. Meanwhile you shall rest and be rewarded for your heroism."

"No," said Bivoj, "I wish to kill it myself, since I myself overcame it!"

Libuše agreed. The people stepped back into a large circle, turning the courtyard into a field of combat, and one of the guards threw a lance with an iron tip at Bivoj's feet. Then with a cry Bivoj cast the boar to the ground. The boar fell on his side but rose with lightning speed, snorted furiously and rushed at Bivoj. The young man moved not an inch until the boar was almost upon him, and then raised his arm and with one mighty blow pierced the boar through the throat. The creature screamed in pain, sank onto its forelegs and rolled on the ground in the throes of death. After a moment it breathed its last. The people rejoiced at Bivoj's victory, each one wanting to touch the hero and shout his praises, and if Libuše had not been there the crowd might have crushed him to death for sheer delight.

That evening a great banquet was held at Vyšehrad in Bivoj's honour. Kazi too praised Bivoj and it was clear she had taken a fancy to the brave and handsome young man. The next morning Kazi asked Bivoj if he would like to join her retinue. Bivoj agreed. It was no great surprise when after a time Kazi and Bivoj married and lived happily ever after.

Horymír

In the times of Prince Křesomysl gold and silver mining grew and flourished mightily. People stopped tilling the fields, left their farms and were easily seduced by the prospect of easy riches. But when the fields lay untended, the land was soon in the grip of hunger. Many local lords were perturbed and sent a delegation headed by Horymír of Neumětely to Vyšehrad to ask the prince to restore order in his domains. The miners in the Příbram mines soon heard of the petition of the lords. They were enraged that Horymír wished to deprive them of their lucrative work and set off to Neumětely to revenge themselves on him. Not finding Horymír in his stronghold, they at least burned the crops in his fields.

When the young lord returned and saw the desolation, he lost no time and that very evening jumped on his horse Šemík and galloped to Příbram. He called to his aid every evil power and spirit, and they helped him fire the miners' homes and fill up the mines with stones and rubble. Then he turned round and rode back, and because Šemík was no ordinary horse, he was home before dawn.

Two days later the furious miners arrived in Vyšehrad and complained about Horymír. Prince Křesomysl had the lord summoned. "Have you heard what the miners accuse you of?" he demanded severely.

Horymír answered, "How could one man alone create such destruction? It is beyond human power. And even if I could have done it, I certainly could not have been back before dawn in my castle, and all my people will testify that I was there!"

But Horymír's defence was in vain, for Křesomysl believed the miners and condemned Horymír to death. He was to be beheaded with a sword immediately.

"I have one last wish," cried Horymír. "My lord, permit me just one last time to ride on my faithful Šemík!"

Křesomysl agreed. Horymír leapt on his horse, whispering something in his ear. The horse whinnied joyfully and Horymír rode him around the courtyard, once, and then twice. All at once Horymír gave a great shout, "Šemík, up!"

With one enormous bound the white horse flew over the battlements and disappeared with the rider into the depths below. People cried out with surprise and hurried to the battlements. How great was their astonishment when they saw Horymír and Šemík galloping away towards Neumětely!

After such an extraordinary deed, all the lords and courtiers begged Křesomysl to pardon Horymír, and eventually the prince allowed himself to be persuaded. Horymír himself then returned to Vyšehrad and confessed everything, as well as explaining why he had acted as he had. Křesomysl acknowledged that he too bore some responsibility for the unfortunate events. He at once decreed that the mining of gold and silver should be cut back, and ordered the people to take more care of their farms. .

The great leap had taken all of Šemík's strength, and now the horse sickened and wasted. When he sensed that his end was near, he asked his master to bury his body at the gate of the courtyard so that even after death they would be close to each other. Horymír granted his wish. In Neumětely you can still see a great stone, the former threshold of Horymír's manor, underneath which, so the legend goes, rests the body of the faithful Šemík.

The Stone Shepherdesses

When the great days of Vyšehrad were gone, the walls and the palace crumbled and were overgrown with weeds, while the animals belonging to the poor cottagers who lived beneath the Vyšehrad Rock pastured on its stony slopes. Among them were the thin goats that the two daughters of a poor widow used to drive to pasture. Their mother always warned the girls not to take the goats to places where the rock dropped away dangerously towards the river. A beast would only have to take one wrong step there, and they would lose their livelihood, since goat's milk was often their only source of sustenance. One day, however, the girls were distracted by their games and the creatures wandered right to the edge of the rock. One of the goats slipped on the stones, the others took fright and with a terrified bleating the whole small flock tumbled down into the Vltava and was drowned. As soon as she caught sight of her daughters the mother realised how it had happened. In despair at the loss of her livelihood she screamed at her daughters. "If only you would just turn into stone for your disobedience!" And the children truly turned to stone. The tears and lamentations of their mother were all in vain, and the girls remained for ever transformed into two little rocks that people began to call the Stone Shepherdesses. They are still standing there today.

The Devil's Stones

Since time immemorial three parts of a broken stone set up in gardens near the Church of St Peter and St Paul have been called the Devil's Stone, or the Devil's Pillar.

Once, long ago, there was a priest serving at the church who was particularly pious and spent all his time caring for the parish. Hearing of him, the devil decided that come what may he must get that priest's soul, for the more honest and pious a man, the greater the value of his soul for the devil. One day the priest was passing by the local tavern, and some of his parishioners called out to him to come and join them there for a while. It seemed foolish to refuse. The neighbours were playing cards over a pitcher and they lured the priest into joining in their game. He won and kept on winning, as if the devil had charmed his cards. When the inn closed, the neighbours insisted that the priest should come again the next day to give them a chance to recover their losses. The priest allowed himself to be persuaded and came. But the devil was present as well. This time the priest lost and kept on losing. He lost all through the evening, and so it struck him as natural that he should come again the next day to recover his losses in his turn. He came once, twice, failed to get his money back but soon had succumbed to the game to the extent that he could think of nothing else. One evening, when yet again the cards were against him, he called on the help of the devil himself. It was the moment the fiend had been waiting for. He appeared to the priest and offered to serve him, but only for three years. Then he would carry the priest off to hell. The priest agreed.

From that time on the priest was always dealt such incredibly lucky cards that it took his fellow players' breath away. Success increased his passion even more, and so as soon as he had haphazardly celebrated mass and taken off his cassock, he would hasten to the neighbours to play cards. As time went by the parish went to rack and ruin, the church was full of dust and cobwebs, and fewer and fewer people came to divine service.

A year went by, and then a second year, and the third year began. As the appointed time drew closer and closer, the priest thought ever more often of his approaching end. On the eve of the day when precisely three years would have passed since his meeting with the devil, the priest stayed in the church after mass, fell down before the altar weeping and implored St. Peter to help him in his misery. St. Peter had mercy on him, and advised him to summon the devil and ask him for a granite pillar from St. Peter's Cathedral in Rome. If the devil could bring it before the priest had finished the morning mass at Vyšehrad, then the sinner's soul would fall into hell, but if the devil was late, the priest would be saved.

The priest did as St. Peter told him. When the devil appeared, the priest asked him in a trembling voice to grant this last wish. With a taunting grin the devil agreed and vanished at once. He flew through the dark night like lighting, and at the stroke of midnight he was already over Rome. He made things a little easier for himself by taking a pillar from the very first church in Rome that he saw; it was the church of Santa Maria i Trastevere, and one pillar is missing from its portico to this day. He hoisted it onto his back and flew back into the sky. But St. Peter never took his eyes off the devil, and when the devil was flying with the pillar over Venice, he burst out of the clouds and threw the pillar down from the devil's shoulder. The pillar fell into the sea and sank down to the very bottom. It took the devil a long time and a lot of puffing and blowing to bring it to the surface, but when he had managed it St. Peter gave him another push and he dropped it again. The same thing happened three times, and meanwhile the sun had risen over Venice. The delay cost the devil so much time that he only reached Vyšehrad at the moment when morning mass in the church had just finished.

The devil saw that he had lost. Angrily he flung the pillar to the ground, where it broke into three pieces, and then he sank down to hell in clouds of stinking smoke. And as for the liberated priest? He reformed, never touched cards again, and whenever he passed a tavern he looked the other way.

Alena Ježková
77 Prague Legends

Illustrations, cover and graphic design by Renáta Fučíková.
Translated from the original Czech by Anna Bryson Gustová.
Edited by Linda Turner.
Czech original edited by PhDr. Anna Novotná.
Type set by Vladimír Vyskočil.
Printed by Europrint a.s., Prague.
Published by Práh s.r.o., Patočkova 2386/85, 169 00 Prague 6,
www.prah.cz in 2006 as its 229. publication.
First Edition.

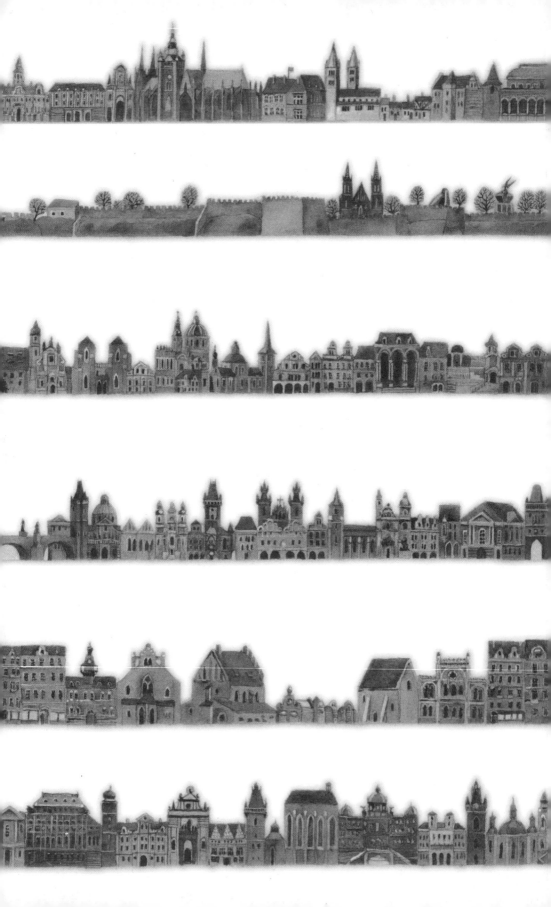